Glencoe
Algebra 1

Integration
Applications
Connections

Studasters

GLENCOE
McGraw-Hill

New York, New York   Columbus, Ohio   Woodland Hills, California   Peoria, Illnois

Glencoe/McGraw-Hill

A Division of The McGraw-Hill Companies

Send all inquiries to:
Glencoe/McGraw-Hill
8787 Orion Place
Columbus, OH 43240-4027

Algebra 1
Study Guide Masters

ISBN: 0-02-824859-7

10 11 12 13 14 15   021   03 02 01 00

Contents

Study Guide

Variables and Expressions

Any letter used to represent an unspecified number is called a variable. You can use variables to translate verbal expressions into algebraic expressions.

Words	Symbols
4 more than a number	$x + 4$
a number decreased by 8	$b - 8$
the product of 5 and a number	$5c$
a number divided by 8	$h \div 8$ or $\frac{h}{8}$
a number squared	y^2

The algebraic expression x^n represents a product in which each factor is the same. The small raised n is the exponent and it tells how many times the base, x, is used as a factor.

Example: Evaluate 3^4.

$$3^4 = 3 \cdot 3 \cdot 3 \cdot 3$$
$$= 81$$

Write a verbal expression for each algebraic expression.

1. $w - 1$

2. $\frac{1}{3}a^3$

3. $81 + 2x$

Write an algebraic expression for each verbal expression.

4. a number decreased by 5

5. four times a number

6. 8 less than a number

7. a number divided by 6

8. a number multiplied by 37

9. the sum of a number and 9

10. 3 less than 5 times a number

11. twice the sum of 15 and a number

12. 7 more than the product of 6 and a number

13. 30 increased by 3 times the square of a number

Write each expression as an expression with exponents.

14. $7 \cdot 7 \cdot 7$

15. $3 \cdot p \cdot p$

16. $9(b)(b)(b)(b)(b)$

Evaluate each expression.

17. 2^3

18. 10^5

19. 4^4

Algebra 1

Study Guide

Variables and Expressions

Any letter used to represent an unspecified number is called a variable. You can use variables to translate verbal expressions into algebraic expressions.

Words	Symbols
4 more than a number	$x + 4$
a number decreased by 8	$b - 8$
the product of 5 and a number	$5c$
a number divided by 8	$h \div 8$ or $\frac{h}{8}$
a number squared	y^2

The algebraic expression x^n represents a product in which each factor is the same. The small raised n is the exponent and it tells how many times the base, x, is used as a factor.

Example: Evaluate 3^4.

$$3^4 = 3 \cdot 3 \cdot 3 \cdot 3$$
$$= 81$$

Answers may vary. Sample answers are given.

Write a verbal expression for each algebraic expression.

1. $w - 1$ **one less than w**

2. $\frac{1}{3}a^3$ **one third the cube of a**

3. $81 + 2x$ **eighty-one increased by twice x**

Write an algebraic expression for each verbal expression.

4. a number decreased by 5 $n - 5$

5. four times a number $4n$

6. 8 less than a number $n - 8$

7. a number divided by 6 $n \div 6$

8. a number multiplied by 37 $37n$

9. the sum of a number and 9 $n + 9$

10. 3 less than 5 times a number $5n - 3$

11. twice the sum of 15 and a number $2(15 + n)$

12. 7 more than the product of 6 and a number $6n + 7$

13. 30 increased by 3 times the square of a number $30 + 3n^2$

Write each expression as an expression with exponents.

14. $7 \cdot 7 \cdot 7$ 7^3

15. $3 \cdot p \cdot p$ $3p^2$

16. $9(b)(b)(b)(b)(b)$ $9b^5$

Evaluate each expression.

17. 2^3 **8**

18. 10^5 **100,000**

19. 4^4 **256**

NAME_____ DATE _____

Study Guide

Patterns and Sequences

When solving certain problems, you must often look for a pattern. A **pattern** is a repeated design or arrangement.

Example 1: Study the pattern at the right.

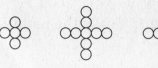

Draw the next three figures in the pattern. The pattern begins by adding one circle to all four sides of the original, then continues by adding an extra circle to all four sides. The next three figures are drawn below.

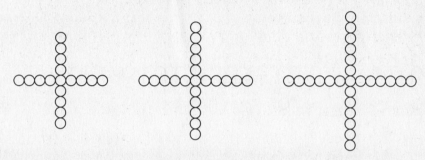

The numbers 1, 3, 5, 7, 9 and 11 form a **sequence.** A sequence is a set of numbers in a specific order. The numbers in a sequence are called **terms.**

Example 2: Find the next three numbers in each sequence.

a. 2, 6, 18, 54, ⋯ Study the pattern in the sequence. Each term is 3 times more than the term before it. The next three terms are 162, 486, and 1,458.

b. 128, 64, 32, ⋯ Study the pattern in the sequence. Each term is $\frac{1}{2}$ of the term before it. The next three terms are 16, 8, and 4.

Give the next two items for each pattern.

1.

2.

3. What color is the 50th figure in Exercise 2? Explain your reasoning.

4. 2, 12, 72, 432, ⋯

5. $b + 1, b + 4, b + 9, b + 16, ⋯$

6. 10, 7, 11, 8, 12, 9, 13, ⋯

Algebra 1

1-2

Study Guide

Patterns and Sequences

When solving certain problems, you must often look for a pattern. A **pattern** is a repeated design or arrangement.

Example 1: Study the pattern at the right.

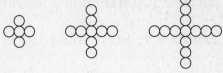

Draw the next three figures in the pattern. The pattern begins by adding one circle to all four sides of the original, then continues by adding an extra circle to all four sides. The next three figures are drawn below.

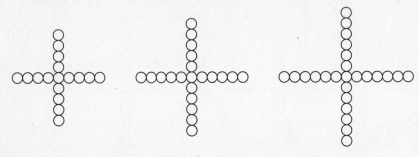

The numbers 1, 3, 5, 7, 9 and 11 form a **sequence.** A sequence is a set of numbers in a specific order. The numbers in a sequence are called **terms.**

Example 2: Find the next three numbers in each sequence.

      a. 2, 6, 18, 54, ⋯ Study the pattern in the sequence. Each term is 3 times more than the term before it. The next three terms are 162, 486, and 1,458.

      b. 128, 64, 32, ⋯ Study the pattern in the sequence. Each term is $\frac{1}{2}$ of the term before it. The next three terms are 16, 8, and 4.

Give the next two items for each pattern.

1.

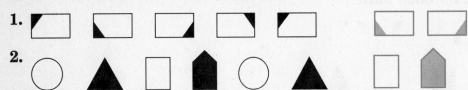

2.

3. What color is the 50th figure in Exercise 2? Explain your reasoning.
   Black; even numbered figures are black.

4. 2, 12, 72, 432, ⋯ **2,592 and 15,552**

5. $b + 1, b + 4, b + 9, b + 16,$ ⋯ $b + 25$ and $b + 36$

6. 10, 7, 11, 8, 12, 9, 13, ⋯ **10 and 14**

1-3

Study Guide

Order of Operations

Ian said Shelley won first prize and I won second prize. Without punctuation, this sentence has three possible meanings.

Ian said, "Shelley won first prize and I won second prize."
or
"Ian," said Shelley, "won first prize and I won second prize."
or
Ian said Shelley won first prize and I [that is, the speaker] won second prize.

In mathematics, in order to avoid confusion about meaning, an agreed-upon order of operations tells us whether a mathematical expression such as $15 - 12 \div 4$ means $(15 - 12) \div 4$ or $15 - (12 \div 4)$. That order is shown at the right.

Order of Operations
1. Simplify expressions inside grouping symbols.
2. Evaluate all powers.
3. Do all multiplications and divisions from left to right.
4. Do all additions and subtractions from left to right.

You can evaluate an algebraic expression when the value of each variable is known. Replace each variable with its value and then use the order of operations to perform the indicated operations. Remember to do all operations within grouping symbols first.

Example 1: Evaluate $15 - 12 \div 4$.

$$15 - 12 \div 4 = 15 - 3$$
$$= 12$$

Example 2: Evaluate $x^3 + 5(y - 3)$ if $x = 2$ and $y = 12$.

$$x^3 + 5(y - 3) = 2^3 + 5(12 - 3)$$
$$= 2^3 + 5(9)$$
$$= 8 + 5(9)$$
$$= 8 + 45$$
$$= 53$$

Evaluate each expression.

1. $10 + 8 \cdot 1$

2. $3^2 \div 3 + 2^2 \cdot 7 - 20 \div 5$

3. $12(20 - 17) - 3 \cdot 6$

4. $\dfrac{15 + 60}{30 - 5}$

Evaluate each expression when $x = 2$, $y = 3$, $a = \dfrac{4}{5}$, and $b = \dfrac{3}{5}$.

5. $x + 7$

6. $3x - 5$

7. $6a + 8b$

8. $a^2 + 2b$

9. $\dfrac{5\,a^2 b}{y}$

10. $(10x)^2 + 100a$

11. $23 - (a + b)$

12. $\dfrac{x^4 - y^2}{3ay}$

3

Study Guide

Order of Operations

Ian said Shelley won first prize and I won second prize. Without punctuation, this sentence has three possible meanings.

Ian said, "Shelley won first prize and I won second prize."

or

"Ian," said Shelley, "won first prize and I won second prize."

or

Ian said Shelley won first prize and I [that is, the speaker] won second prize.

In mathematics, in order to avoid confusion about meaning, an agreed-upon order of operations tells us whether a mathematical expression such as $15 - 12 \div 4$ means $(15 - 12) \div 4$ or $15 - (12 \div 4)$. That order is shown at the right.

Order of Operations
1. Simplify expressions inside grouping symbols.
2. Evaluate all powers.
3. Do all multiplications and divisions from left to right.
4. Do all additions and subtractions from left to right.

You can evaluate an algebraic expression when the value of each variable is known. Replace each variable with its value and then use the order of operations to perform the indicated operations. Remember to do all operations within grouping symbols first.

Example 1: Evaluate $15 - 12 \div 4$.

$$15 - 12 \div 4 = 15 - 3$$
$$= 12$$

Example 2: Evaluate $x^3 + 5(y - 3)$ if $x = 2$ and $y = 12$.

$$x^3 + 5(y - 3) = 2^3 + 5(12 - 3)$$
$$= 2^3 + 5(9)$$
$$= 8 + 5(9)$$
$$= 8 + 45$$
$$= 53$$

Evaluate each expression.

1. $10 + 8 \cdot 1$ **18**

2. $3^2 \div 3 + 2^2 \cdot 7 - 20 \div 5$ **27**

3. $12(20 - 17) - 3 \cdot 6$ **18**

4. $\dfrac{15 + 60}{30 - 5}$ **3**

Evaluate each expression when $x = 2$, $y = 3$, $a = \dfrac{4}{5}$, and $b = \dfrac{3}{5}$.

5. $x + 7$ **9**

6. $3x - 5$ **1**

7. $6a + 8b$ $\dfrac{48}{5}$**, or** $9\dfrac{3}{5}$

8. $a^2 + 2b$ $\dfrac{46}{25}$**, or** $1\dfrac{21}{25}$

9. $\dfrac{5a^2b}{y}$ $\dfrac{16}{25}$

10. $(10x)^2 + 100a$ **480**

11. $23 - (a + b)$ $\dfrac{108}{5}$**, or** $21\dfrac{3}{5}$

12. $\dfrac{x^4 - y^2}{3ay}$ $\dfrac{35}{36}$

Integration: Statistics
Stem-and-Leaf Plots

Mrs. Corrigan interviewed some students who were willing to help her with some typing. The number of words typed per minute by each student is listed below.

| 20 | 19 | 18 | 16 | 17 | 17 | 14 |

This data can be organized on a **stem-and-leaf plot.** The greatest common place value of each piece of data is used to form the **stem.** The next greatest place value is used to form the **leaves.**

Stem	Leaf
1	9 8 6 7 7 4
2	0

1|8 represents a rate of 18 words per minute.

Data with more than two digits may be rounded $13.5 \Rightarrow 14$ or truncated $13.5 \Rightarrow 13$.

The rounded and truncated values of the data at the right can be compared in a back-to-back stem-and-leaf plot.

61.5	51.9	60.0
46.0	38.5	39.1
56.2	33.0	61.5
65.4	51.0	52.3

Rounded	Stem	Truncated
9 9 3	3	3 8 9
6	4	6
6 2 2 1	5	1 1 2 6
5 2 2 0	6	0 1 1 5

In a back-to-back stem-and-leaf plot, the same stem is used for the leaves of both plots.

Solve each problem.

1. The stem-and-leaf plot at the right shows the height, in feet, of buildings in San Francisco that are over 500 ft tall.
   a. How tall is the tallest building?
   b. What is the height of the shortest building that is taller than 500 ft?
   c. What building height occurs most frequently?

Stem	Leaf
5	2 3 3 4 5 6 7 7 7
6	
7	8
8	5

5|6 represents a height of 560 feet.

2. Lori sells tickets at a movie theater. Her sales for week 1 were $173, $194, $160, $182, $183, and $247. Sales for week 2 were $137, $182, $151, $193, $199, and $194.
   a. Make a stem-and-leaf plot of two weeks' sales. Round the data to the nearest $10.
   b. What is the most amount of money made in one day during the two week period?

Stem	Leaf

Study Guide

Integration: Statistics
Stem-and-Leaf Plots

Mrs. Corrigan interviewed some students who were willing to help her with some typing. The number of words typed per minute by each student is listed below.

| 20 | 19 | 18 | 16 | 17 | 17 | 14 |

This data can be organized on a **stem-and-leaf plot.** The greatest common place value of each piece of data is used to form the **stem.** The next greatest place value is used to form the **leaves.**

Stem	Leaf
1	9 8 6 7 7 4
2	0

1|8 represents a rate of 18 words per minute.

Data with more than two digits may be rounded
$13.5 \Rightarrow 14$ or truncated $13.\cancel{5} \Rightarrow 13$.

The rounded and truncated values of the data at the right can be compared in a back-to-back stem-and-leaf plot.

61.5	51.9	60.0
46.0	38.5	39.1
56.2	33.0	61.5
65.4	51.0	52.3

Rounded	Stem	Truncated
9 9 3	3	3 8 9
6	4	6
6 2 2 1	5	1 1 2 6
5 2 2 0	6	0 1 1 5

In a back-to-back stem-and-leaf plot, the same stem is used for the leaves of both plots.

Solve each problem.

1. The stem-and-leaf plot at the right shows the height, in feet, of buildings in San Francisco that are over 500 ft tall.
   a. How tall is the tallest building? **850 ft**
   b. What is the height of the shortest building that is taller than 500 ft? **520 ft**
   c. What building height occurs most frequently? **570 ft**

Stem	Leaf
5	2 3 3 4 5 6 7 7 7
6	
7	8
8	5

5|6 represents a height of 560 feet.

2. Lori sells tickets at a movie theater. Her sales for week 1 were $173, $194, $160, $182, $183, and $247. Sales for week 2 were $137, $182, $151, $193, $199, and $194.
   a. Make a stem-and-leaf plot of two weeks' sales. Round the data to the nearest $10.
   b. What is the most amount of money made in one day during the two week period? **$247**

Stem	Leaf
1	4 5 6 7 8 8 8 9 9 9
2	0 5

1|6 represents $160-$169.

Open Sentences

Mathematical statements with one or more variables are called **open sentences.** Open sentences are **solved** by finding a replacement for the variable that results in a true sentence. The replacement is called a **solution.**

Example 1: Replace a in $3a + 12 = 39$ with the value 9.

$$3a + 12 = 39$$
$$3(9) + 12 = 39$$
$$27 + 12 = 39$$
$$39 = 39 \quad \text{true}$$

Since $a = 9$ makes the sentence $3a + 12 = 39$ true, 9 is a solution.

A set of numbers from which replacements for a variable may be chosen is called a **replacement set.** The set of all replacements for the variable in an open sentence that results in a true sentence is called the **solution set** for the sentence.

A sentence that contains an equals sign, $=$, is called an **equation** and sometimes may be solved by simply applying the order of operations. A sentence having the symbols $<$ or $>$ is called an **inequality.**

Example 2: Solve $\dfrac{2(3 + 1)}{3(2 + 1)} = b$.

$$\frac{2(3 + 1)}{3(2 + 1)} = b$$
$$\frac{2(4)}{3(3)} = b$$
$$\frac{8}{9} = b$$

State whether each equation is <u>true</u> or <u>false</u> for the value of the variable given.

1. $y + \dfrac{1}{2} = \dfrac{1}{4} + \dfrac{1}{2}, y = \dfrac{7}{2}$

2. $x^4 = 2^8, x = 4$

3. $a^2 + a^3 + 2 < 10, a = 2$

4. $\dfrac{2^3 - 2d}{3^2 - 1} \le 2, d = 2$

Find the solution set for each inequality if the replacement sets are $x = \{\frac{1}{2}, 2, 3, \frac{1}{4}\}$ and $y = \{2, 4, 6, 8\}$.

5. $x + 4 < 6$

6. $3y \ge 18$

7. $\dfrac{y}{3} > 1$

Solve each equation.

8. $s = \dfrac{15 - 6}{27 - 24}$

9. $w = 6^2 - 3^3$

10. $c = 3\dfrac{1}{2} + 2\dfrac{1}{4}$

Study Guide

Open Sentences

Mathematical statements with one or more variables are called **open sentences.** Open sentences are **solved** by finding a replacement for the variable that results in a true sentence. The replacement is called a **solution.**

Example 1: Replace a in $3a + 12 = 39$ with the value 9.

$$3a + 12 = 39$$
$$3(9) + 12 = 39$$
$$27 + 12 = 39$$
$$39 = 39 \quad \text{true}$$

Since $a = 9$ makes the sentence $3a + 12 = 39$ true, 9 is a solution.

A set of numbers from which replacements for a variable may be chosen is called a **replacement set.** The set of all replacements for the variable in an open sentence that results in a true sentence is called the **solution set** for the sentence.

A sentence that contains an equals sign, $=$, is called an **equation** and sometimes may be solved by simply applying the order of operations. A sentence having the symbols $<$ or $>$ is called an **inequality.**

Example 2: Solve $\dfrac{2(3 + 1)}{3(2 + 1)} = b.$

$$\frac{2(3 + 1)}{3(2 + 1)} = b$$
$$\frac{2(4)}{3(3)} = b$$
$$\frac{8}{9} = b$$

State whether each equation is _true_ or _false_ for the value of the variable given.

1. $y + \dfrac{1}{2} = \dfrac{1}{4} + \dfrac{1}{2}, y = \dfrac{7}{2}$ **False**

2. $x^4 = 2^8, x = 4$ **True**

3. $a^2 + a^3 + 2 < 10, a = 2$ **False**

4. $\dfrac{2^3 - 2d}{3^2 - 1} \leq 2, d = 2$ **True**

Find the solution set for each inequality if the replacement sets are $x = \{\frac{1}{2}, 2, 3, \frac{1}{4}\}$ and $y = \{2, 4, 6, 8\}$.

5. $x + 4 < 6$ $\left\{\dfrac{1}{2}, \dfrac{1}{4}\right\}$

6. $3y \geq 18$ **{6, 8}**

7. $\dfrac{y}{3} > 1$ **{4, 6, 8}**

Solve each equation.

8. $s = \dfrac{15 - 6}{27 - 24}$ **3**

9. $w = 6^2 - 3^3$ **9**

10. $c = 3\dfrac{1}{2} + 2\dfrac{1}{4}$ $5\dfrac{3}{4}$

Study Guide

Identity and Equality Properties

The identity and equality properties in the chart below can help you solve algebraic equations and evaluate mathematical expressions.

Additive Identity Property	For any number a, $a + 0 = 0 + a = a$.
Multiplicative Identity Property	For any number a, $a \cdot 1 = 1 \cdot a = a$.
Multiplicative Property of Zero	For any number a, $a \cdot 0 = 0 \cdot a = 0$.
Substitution Property	For any numbers a and b, if $a = b$ then a may be replaced by b.
Reflexive Property	$a = a$
Symmetric Property	If $a = b$, then $b = a$.
Transitive Property	If $a = b$ and $b = c$, then $a = c$.

Example: Evaluate $24 \cdot 1 - 8 + 5(9 \div 3 - 3)$. Indicate the property used in each step.

$$
\begin{aligned}
24 \cdot 1 - 8 + 5(9 \div 3 - 3) &= 24 \cdot 1 - 8 + 5(3 - 3) && \text{Substitution (=)} \\
&= 24 \cdot 1 - 8 + 5(0) && \text{Substitution (=)} \\
&= 24 - 8 + 5(0) && \text{Multiplicative identity} \\
&= 24 - 8 + 0 && \text{Multiplication property of zero} \\
&= 16 + 0 && \text{Substitution (=)} \\
&= 16 && \text{Additive identity}
\end{aligned}
$$

Solve each equation.

1. $a(9) = 0$ **2.** $15 \cdot m = 15$ **3.** $0 + p = 3$ **4.** $7(0) = y$

Name the property or properties illustrated by each statement.

5. $0 + 21 = 21$ **6.** $(0)15 = 0$ **7.** If $4 + 5 = 9$, then $9 = 4 + 5$.

8. $(1)94 = 94$ **9.** If $3 + 3 = 6$ and $6 = 3 \cdot 2$, then $3 + 3 = 3 \cdot 2$.

10. $(14 - 6) + 3 = 8 + 3$ **11.** $23 \cdot 1 = 23$ **12.** $4 + 3 = 4 + 3$

Evaluate each expression. Name the property used in each step.

13. $10 \div 5 - 2^2 \div 2 + 13$ **14.** $3(5 - 5 \cdot 1^2) + 21 \div 7$

Study Guide

Identity and Equality Properties

The identity and equality properties in the chart below can help you solve algebraic equations and evaluate mathematical expressions.

Additive Identity Property	For any number a, $a + 0 = 0 + a = a$.
Multiplicative Identity Property	For any number a, $a \cdot 1 = 1 \cdot a = a$.
Multiplicative Property of Zero	For any number a, $a \cdot 0 = 0 \cdot a = 0$.
Substitution Property	For any numbers a and b, if $a = b$ then a may be replaced by b.
Reflexive Property	$a = a$
Symmetric Property	If $a = b$, then $b = a$.
Transitive Property	If $a = b$ and $b = c$, then $a = c$.

Example: Evaluate $24 \cdot 1 - 8 + 5(9 \div 3 - 3)$. Indicate the property used in each step.

$$24 \cdot 1 - 8 + 5(9 \div 3 - 3) = 24 \cdot 1 - 8 + 5(3 - 3) \quad \text{Substitution (=)}$$
$$= 24 \cdot 1 - 8 + 5(0) \quad \text{Substitution (=)}$$
$$= 24 - 8 + 5(0) \quad \text{Multiplicative identity}$$
$$= 24 - 8 + 0 \quad \text{Multiplication property of zero}$$
$$= 16 + 0 \quad \text{Substitution (=)}$$
$$= 16 \quad \text{Additive identity}$$

Solve each equation.

1. $a(9) = 0$
   0

2. $15 \cdot m = 15$
   1

3. $0 + p = 3$
   3

4. $7(0) = y$
   0

Name the property or properties illustrated by each statement.

5. $0 + 21 = 21$
   Add. identity

6. $(0)15 = 0$
   Mult. Prop. of Zero

7. If $4 + 5 = 9$,
   then $9 = 4 + 5$.
   Symmetric Prop.

8. $(1)94 = 94$
   Mult. identity

9. If $3 + 3 = 6$ and $6 = 3 \cdot 2$, then $3 + 3 = 3 \cdot 2$.
   Transitive Property

10. $(14 - 6) + 3 = 8 + 3$
    Substitution

11. $23 \cdot 1 = 23$
    Mult. identity

12. $4 + 3 = 4 + 3$
    Reflexive Prop.

Evaluate each expression. Name the property used in each step.

13. $10 \div 5 - 2^2 \div 2 + 13$
    $= 10 \div 5 - 4 \div 2 + 13$ Sub. (=)
    $= 2 - 4 \div 2 + 13$ Sub. (=)
    $= 2 - 2 + 13$ Sub. (=)
    $= 0 + 13$ Sub. (=)
    $= 13$ Add. identity

14. $3(5 - 5 \cdot 1^2) + 21 \div 7$
    $= 3(5 - 5 \cdot 1) + 21 \div 7$ Sub. (=)
    $= 3(5 - 5) + 21 \div 7$ Mult. identity
    $= 3(0) + 21 \div 7$ Sub. (=)
    $= 0 + 21 \div 7$ Mult. Prop. of Zero
    $= 0 + 3$ Sub. (=)
    $= 3$ Add. identity

1-7

Study Guide

The Distributive Property

When you find the product of two integers, you find the sum of two partial products. For example, you can write

$$
\begin{array}{r}
58 \\
\times\ 5 \\
\hline
290
\end{array}
\quad \text{as} \quad
\begin{array}{r}
50 + 8 \\
\times\qquad 5 \\
\hline
250 + 40
\end{array}
\leftarrow (50 \times 5) + (8 \times 5)
$$

The statement $(50 + 8) \times 5 = (50 \times 5) + (8 \times 5)$ illustrates the distributive property. The multiplier 5 is distributed over the 50 and the 8.

Distributive Property
For any numbers *a*, *b*, and *c*, $a(b + c) = ab + ac$ and $(b + c)a = ba + ca$; $a(b - c) = ab - ac$ and $(b - c)a = ba - bc$.

You can use the distributive property to simplify algebraic expressions.

Example: Simplify $4(a^2 + 3ab) - ab$.

$$
\begin{aligned}
4(a^2 + 3ab) - ab &= 4(a^2 + 3ab) - 1ab && \text{Multiplicative identity} \\
&= 4a^2 + 12ab - 1ab && \text{Distributive property} \\
&= 4a^2 + (12 - 1)ab && \text{Distributive property} \\
&= 4a^2 + 11ab && \text{Substitution}
\end{aligned}
$$

Name the coefficient of each term. Then name the like terms in each list of terms.

1. $3x,\ 3x^2,\ 5x$

2. $2mn,\ 10mn^2,\ 12mn^2,\ mn^2$

Use the distributive property to find each product.

3. $4 \cdot 315$

4. $3 \cdot 24$

Use the distributive property to rewrite each expression.

5. $5(4x - 9)$

6. $9r^2 + 9s^2$

Simplify each expression, if possible. If not possible, write in simplest form.

7. $7b + 3b$

8. $4(5ac - 7)$

9. $21c + 18c + 31b - 3b$

10. $10x^2 - 6x^3$

11. $10xy - 4(xy + xy)$

12. $0.2(0.8 + 7y) + 0.36y$

Algebra 1

Study Guide

The Distributive Property

When you find the product of two integers, you find the sum of two partial products. For example, you can write

$$\begin{array}{r} 58 \\ \times\ 5 \\ \hline 290 \end{array} \quad \text{as} \quad \begin{array}{r} 50 + 8 \\ \times\ \quad 5 \\ \hline 250 + 40 \end{array} \leftarrow (50 \times 5) + (8 \times 5)$$

The statement $(50 + 8) \times 5 = (50 \times 5) + (8 \times 5)$ illustrates the distributive property. The multiplier 5 is distributed over the 50 and the 8.

Distributive Property
For any numbers a, b, and c, $a(b + c) = ab + ac$ and $(b + c)a = ba + ca$; $a(b - c) = ab - ac$ and $(b - c)a = ba - bc$.

You can use the distributive property to simplify algebraic expressions.

Example: Simplify $4(a^2 + 3ab) - ab$.

$4(a^2 + 3ab) - ab = 4(a^2 + 3ab) - 1ab$	Multiplicative identity
$= 4a^2 + 12ab - 1ab$	Distributive property
$= 4a^2 + (12 - 1)ab$	Distributive property
$= 4a^2 + 11ab$	Substitution

Name the coefficient of each term. Then name the like terms in each list of terms.

1. $3x, 3x^2, 5x$ **3, 3, 5; 3x, 5x**

2. $2mn, 10mn^2, 12mn^2, mn^2$
 2, 10, 12, 1; 10mn², 12mn², mn²

Use the distributive property to find each product.

3. $4 \cdot 315$ **1260**

4. $3 \cdot 24$ **72**

Use the distributive property to rewrite each expression.

5. $5(4x - 9)$ **20x − 45**

6. $9r^2 + 9s^2$ **9(r² + s²)**

Simplify each expression, if possible. If not possible, write in simplest form.

7. $7b + 3b$ **10b**

8. $4(5ac - 7)$
 20ac − 28

9. $21c + 18c + 31b - 3b$
 39c + 28b

10. $10x^2 - 6x^3$
 in simplest form

11. $10xy - 4(xy + xy)$
 2xy

12. $0.2(0.8 + 7y) + 0.36y$
 0.16 + 1.76y

NAME_____ DATE _____

Study Guide

Commutative and Associative Properties

The commutative and associative properties can be used to simplify expressions.

Commutative Properties
For any numbers a and b, $a + b = b + a$ and $a \cdot b = b \cdot a$.

Associative Properties
For any numbers a, b, and c, $(a + b) + c = a + (b + c)$ and $(ab)c = a(bc)$.

Example: Simplify $8(y + 2x) + 7y$.

$$8(y + 2x) + 7y = (8y + 16x) + 7y \qquad \text{Distributive property}$$
$$= (16x + 8y) + 7y \qquad \text{Commutative property of addition}$$
$$= 16x + (8y + 7y) \qquad \text{Associative property of addition}$$
$$= 16x + (8 + 7)y \qquad \text{Distributive property}$$
$$= 16x + 15y \qquad \text{Substitution property of equality}$$

Simplify.

1. $4x + 3y + x$

2. $8r^2s + 2rs^2 + 7r^2s$

3. $6(2x + 4y) + 2(x + 9)$

4. $3a^2 + 4b + 10a^2$

5. $4xy + 7x^2y + xy$

6. $3ab + 4a^2b + 5(2a^2b)$

7. $6(a + b) - a + 3b$

8. $0.5(18x + 16y) + 13x$

9. $\frac{2}{3} + \frac{1}{2}(x + 10) + \frac{4}{3}$

10. $5(0.3x + 0.1y) + 0.2x$

11. $5(2y + 3x) + 6(y + x)$

12. $z^2 + 9x^2 + \frac{4}{3}z^2 + \frac{1}{3}x^2$

Name the property illustrated by each statement.

13. $6x + 2y = 2y + 6x$

14. $15(a + 4) = 15a + 15(4)$

15. $1 \cdot b^3 = b^3$

16. $(2c + 6) + 10 = 2c + (6 + 10)$

Algebra 1

Study Guide

Commutative and Associative Properties

The commutative and associative properties can be used to simplify expressions.

Commutative Properties	Associative Properties
For any numbers a and b, $a + b = b + a$ and $a \cdot b = b \cdot a$.	For any numbers a, b, and c, $(a + b) + c = a + (b + c)$ and $(ab)c = a(bc)$.

Example: Simplify $8(y + 2x) + 7y$.

$$
\begin{aligned}
8(y + 2x) + 7y &= (8y + 16x) + 7y && \text{Distributive property} \\
&= (16x + 8y) + 7y && \text{Commutative property of addition} \\
&= 16x + (8y + 7y) && \text{Associative property of addition} \\
&= 16x + (8 + 7)y && \text{Distributive property} \\
&= 16x + 15y && \text{Substitution property of equality}
\end{aligned}
$$

Simplify.

1. $4x + 3y + x$
   $5x + 3y$

2. $8r^2s + 2rs^2 + 7r^2s$
   $15r^2s + 2rs^2$

3. $6(2x + 4y) + 2(x + 9)$
   $14x + 24y + 18$

4. $3a^2 + 4b + 10a^2$
   $13a^2 + 4b$

5. $4xy + 7x^2y + xy$
   $5xy + 7x^2y$

6. $3ab + 4a^2b + 5(2a^2b)$
   $14a^2b + 3ab$

7. $6(a + b) - a + 3b$
   $5a + 9b$

8. $0.5(18x + 16y) + 13x$
   $22x + 8y$

9. $\frac{2}{3} + \frac{1}{2}(x + 10) + \frac{4}{3}$
   $7 + \frac{1}{2}x$

10. $5(0.3x + 0.1y) + 0.2x$
    $1.7x + 0.5y$

11. $5(2y + 3x) + 6(y + x)$
    $16y + 21x$

12. $z^2 + 9x^2 + \frac{4}{3}z^2 + \frac{1}{3}x^2$
    $\frac{7}{3}z^2 + \frac{28}{3}x^2$, or
    $2\frac{1}{3}z^2 + 9\frac{1}{3}x^2$

Name the property illustrated by each statement.

13. $6x + 2y = 2y + 6x$ **Commutative property of addition**

14. $15(a + 4) = 15a + 15(4)$
    Distributive property

15. $1 \cdot b^3 = b^3$
    Multiplicative identify

16. $(2c + 6) + 10 = 2c + (6 + 10)$
    Associative property of addition

NAME_____ DATE _____

Study Guide

A Preview of Graphs and Functions

A plane is landing from an altitude of 35,000 ft. The plane descends at a rate of 3,200 ft/min. Mathematically, the plane's altitude can be defined by the following open sentence.

altitude = 35,000 − 3,200t, where t is the time of descent

The table at the right shows the plane's altitude over a period of 3 minutes.

Time of Descent	Plane's Altitude
0 min	35,000
1 min	31,800
2 min	28,600
3 min	25,400

This information can also be represented in a graph. The graph shows the relationship between the plane's altitude and its time of descent.

Example 1:

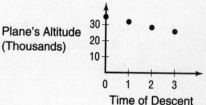

You can use a graph without scales on either axes to show the general shape of the graph that represents a situation.

Example 2: Kelley walks up a hill at a steady pace. Then she runs down the hill. Make a sketch of the graph of the situation.

a.
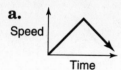

b.
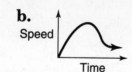

c.
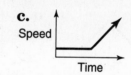

To select the graph that best represents this situation, find the graph that shows a steady pace, followed by an increase in speed. Graph c matches this description.

1. Identify the graph that matches the following statement. Explain your answer. Your body temperature rises as you exercise.

a.
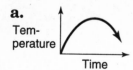

b.

c.
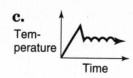

Sketch a reasonable graph for each situation.

2. Tim is riding his bike at a steady pace. Then he has a flat tire. He walks up a hill to a gas station to have the tire fixed. When the tire is fixed, he continues his ride.

3. Ken likes to trade marbles. During the first week of the month, he added lots of marbles to his collection. Then during the next three weeks of the month, he lost several others.

Study Guide

A Preview of Graphs and Functions

A plane is landing from an altitude of 35,000 ft. The plane descends at a rate of 3,200 ft/min. Mathematically, the plane's altitude can be defined by the following open sentence.

altitude = $35,000 - 3,200t$, where t is the time of descent

The table at the right shows the plane's altitude over a period of 3 minutes.

Time of Descent	Plane's Altitude
0 min	35,000
1 min	31,800
2 min	28,600
3 min	25,400

This information can also be represented in a graph. The graph shows the relationship between the plane's altitude and its time of descent.

Example 1:

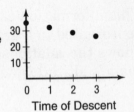

You can use a graph without scales on either axes to show the general shape of the graph that represents a situation.

Example 2: Kelley walks up a hill at a steady pace. Then she runs down the hill. Make a sketch of the graph of the situation.

a.    **b.** 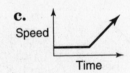   **c.**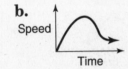

To select the graph that best represents this situation, find the graph that shows a steady pace, followed by an increase in speed. Graph c matches this description.

1. Identify the graph that matches the following statement. Explain your answer. Your body temperature rises as you exercise. **b. You start out with a normal temperature and after time it increases.**

a. 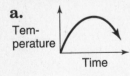   **b.** 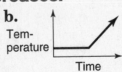   **c.**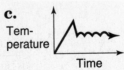

Sketch a reasonable graph for each situation.

2. Tim is riding his bike at a steady pace. Then he has a flat tire. He walks up a hill to a gas station to have the tire fixed. When the tire is fixed, he continues his ride.

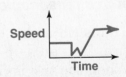

3. Ken likes to trade marbles. During the first week of the month, he added lots of marbles to his collection. Then during the next three weeks of the month, he lost several others.

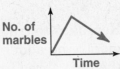

Algebra 1

Integers and the Number Line

The figure at the right is part of a number line. On a number line, the distances marked to the right of 0 are named by members of the set of **whole numbers.**

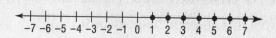

The set of numbers used to name the points marked on the number line at the right is called the set of **integers.**

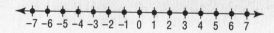

To graph a set of numbers means to locate the points named by those numbers on the number line. The number that corresponds to a point on the number line is called the **coordinate** of the point.

Name the coordinate of point G.

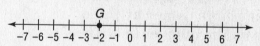

The coordinate of G is -2.

A number line is often used to show addition of integers. For example, to find the sum of 3 and -5, follow the steps at the right.

Step 1 Draw an arrow, starting at 0 and going to 3.
Step 2 Start at 3. Draw an arrow 5 units to the left.
Step 3 The second arrow points to the sum, -2.

Name the coordinate of each point.

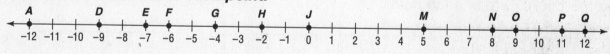

1. M
2. Q
3. H
4. E
5. J
6. A

7. G
8. P
9. F
10. N
11. O
12. D

Graph each set of numbers on a number line.

13. $\{-3, -1, 1, 3\}$

14. $\{-5, -2, 1, 4\}$

15. {integers less than 0}

16. $\{0, 1, 3, 5\}$

17. $\{-3, -2, 2\}$

18. $\{\cdots, -2, -1, 0, 1\}$

Find each sum. If necessary, use a number line.

19. $2 + 3$

20. $9 + 1$

21. $-5 + (-1)$

22. $-10 + 6$

23. $9 + (-9)$

24. $0 + (-4)$

25. $-8 + (-3)$

26. $6 + (-10)$

27. $-6 + 6$

10

Algebra 1

NAME_____ DATE _____

Study Guide

Integers and the Number Line

The figure at the right is part of a number line. On a number line, the distances marked to the right of 0 are named by members of the set of **whole numbers.**

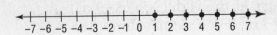

The set of numbers used to name the points marked on the number line at the right is called the set of **integers.**

To graph a set of numbers means to locate the points named by those numbers on the number line. The number that corresponds to a point on the number line is called the **coordinate** of the point.

Name the coordinate of point G.

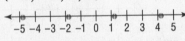

The coordinate of G is -2.

A number line is often used to show addition of integers. For example, to find the sum of 3 and -5, follow the steps at the right.

Step 1 Draw an arrow, starting at 0 and going to 3.
Step 2 Start at 3. Draw an arrow 5 units to the left.
Step 3 The second arrow points to the sum, -2.

Name the coordinate of each point.

1. M **5** 2. Q **12** 3. H **-2** 4. E **-7** 5. J **0** 6. A **-12**

7. G **-4** 8. P **11** 9. F **-6** 10. N **8** 11. O **9** 12. D **-9**

Graph each set of numbers on a number line.

13. $\{-3, -1, 1, 3\}$

14. $\{-5, -2, 1, 4\}$

15. {integers less than 0}

16. $\{0, 1, 3, 5\}$

17. $\{-3, -2, 2\}$

18. $\{\cdots, -2, -1, 0, 1\}$

Find each sum. If necessary, use a number line.

19. $2 + 3$ **5**

20. $9 + 1$ **10**

21. $-5 + (-1)$ **-6**

22. $-10 + 6$ **-4**

23. $9 + (-9)$ **0**

24. $0 + (-4)$ **-4**

25. $-8 + (-3)$ **-11**

26. $6 + (-10)$ **-4**

27. $-6 + 6$ **0**

Algebra 1

2-2

Study Guide

Integration: Statistics
Line Plots

The table to the right shows the final results of the Great Frog Competition in Dickerson County. The frog jumps were measured in inches.

	Jumps		
Frogs	**1**	**2**	**3**
Slippery	61.5	51.9	60.0
Spots	46.0	38.5	39.1
Inky	56.2	33.0	61.5
Popper	65.4	51.0	52.3

Numerical information displayed on a number line is called a **line plot**. The line plot below is another way to show the data for the frog jumping contest.

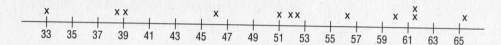

1. Make a table comparing the highest mountains in the United States: Mt. McKinley, 20,633 ft; Mt. Elbert, 14,433 ft; Mt. Rainier, 14,410 ft; Humphrey Peak, 12,633 ft; Kings Peak, 13,528 ft.

Mountain	Height (feet)

Use the table at the right for Exercises 2–4.

2. Make a line plot representing the weights of wrestlers. Insert labels and "x"s on the number line below.

Weights of Junior Varsity Wrestlers (pounds)				
170	160	135	135	160
122	188	154	108	135
140	122	103	190	154

3. How many wrestlers are in weight classes over 140 lb?

4. What is the greatest weight class?

NAME_____ DATE _____

Study Guide

Integration: Statistics
Line Plots

The table to the right shows the final
results of the Great Frog Competition in
Dickerson County. The frog jumps were
measured in inches.

Jumps			
Frogs	**1**	**2**	**3**
Slippery	61.5	51.9	60.0
Spots	46.0	38.5	39.1
Inky	56.2	33.0	61.5
Popper	65.4	51.0	52.3

Numerical information displayed on a number line is called a
line plot. The line plot below is another way to show the data
for the frog jumping contest.

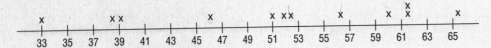

1. Make a table comparing the
   highest mountains in the United
   States: Mt. McKinley, 20,633 ft;
   Mt. Elbert, 14,433 ft; Mt. Rainier,
   14,410 ft; Humphrey Peak,
   12,633 ft; Kings Peak, 13,528 ft.

Mountain	Height (feet)
Mt. McKinley	20,633
Mt. Elbert	14,433
Mt. Rainier	14,410
Humphrey Peak	12,633
Kings Peak	13,528

**Use the table at the right for
Exercises 2–4.**

2. Make a line plot representing the
   weights of wrestlers. Insert labels
   and "x"s on the number line
   below.

Weights of Junior Varsity Wrestlers (pounds)				
170	160	135	135	160
122	188	154	108	135
140	122	103	190	154

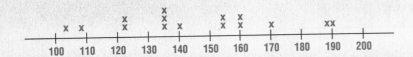

3. How many wrestlers are in weight classes over 140 lb? **7**

4. What is the greatest weight class? **190 lb**

NAME_____ DATE _____

Study Guide

Adding and Subtracting Integers

Use the following definitions, rules, and properties when adding or subtracting integers.

Definition, Rule, or Property		Example
Definition of Absolute Value	For any real number a: if $a > 0$, then $|a| = a$, and if $a < 0$, then $|a| = -a$. $|0| = 0$	$|2| = 2$ $|-2| = 2$
Adding Integers with the Same Sign	To add integers with the same sign, add their absolute values. Give the sum the same sign as the addends.	$3 + 2 = 5$ $-3 + (-2) = -5$
Adding Integers with Different Signs	To add integers with different signs, subtract the lesser absolute value from the greater absolute value. Give the result the same sign as the addend with the greater absolute value.	$-7 + 6 = -1$ $8 + (-4) = 4$
Additive Inverse Property	For every number a, $a + (-a) = 0$.	$-9 + 9 = 0$
Subtraction Rule	To subtract a number, add its additive inverse. For any numbers a and b, $a - b = a + (-b)$.	$8 - (-2) = 8 + 2$ $= 10$

You can use the distributive property and the addition and subtraction rules for integers to simplify expressions with like terms.

Example: Simplify $-6x - x + 9x$.
$$-6x - x + 9x = -6x + (-1x) + 9x$$
$$= [-6 + (-1) + 9]x$$
$$= (-7 + 9)x$$
$$= 2x$$

Find each sum or difference.

1. $-17 + (-16)$

2. $107 + (-40)$

3. $75 + 86$

4. $11 - 41$

5. $15 - (-21)$

6. $-33 - (-17)$

7. $3m + (-15m) - 11m$

8. $-6a + 15a + (-11a)$

9. $-9y + 20y - (-6y)$

Evaluate each expression if $x = -4$, $y = 3$, and $z = -7$.

10. $456 + |z|$

11. $z + (-71) + |y|$

12. $-11 - |x|$

13. $31 - y - |x|$

Algebra 1

NAME _____ DATE _____

Study Guide

Adding and Subtracting Integers

Use the following definitions, rules, and properties when adding or subtracting integers.

Definition, Rule, or Property		Example
Definition of Absolute Value	For any real number a: if $a > 0$, then $|a| = a$, and if $a < 0$, then $|a| = -a$. $|0| = 0$	$|2| = 2$ $|-2| = 2$
Adding Integers with the Same Sign	To add integers with the same sign, add their absolute values. Give the sum the same sign as the addends.	$3 + 2 = 5$ $-3 + (-2) = -5$
Adding Integers with Different Signs	To add integers with different signs, subtract the lesser absolute value from the greater absolute value. Give the result the same sign as the addend with the greater absolute value.	$-7 + 6 = -1$ $8 + (-4) = 4$
Additive Inverse Property	For every number a, $a + (-a) = 0$.	$-9 + 9 = 0$
Subtraction Rule	To subtract a number, add its additive inverse. For any numbers a and b, $a - b = a + (-b)$.	$8 - (-2) = 8 + 2$ $= 10$

You can use the distributive property and the addition and subtraction rules for integers to simplify expressions with like terms.

Example: Simplify $-6x - x + 9x$.
$$-6x - x + 9x = -6x + (-1x) + 9x$$
$$= [-6 + (-1) + 9]x$$
$$= (-7 + 9)x$$
$$= 2x$$

Find each sum or difference.

1. $-17 + (-16)$
−33

2. $107 + (-40)$
67

3. $75 + 86$
161

4. $11 - 41$
−30

5. $15 - (-21)$
36

6. $-33 - (-17)$
−16

7. $3m + (-15m) - 11m$
−23m

8. $-6a + 15a + (-11a)$
−2a

9. $-9y + 20y - (-6y)$
17y

Evaluate each expression if $x = -4$, $y = 3$, and $z = -7$.

10. $456 + |z|$
463

11. $z + (-71) + |y|$
−75

12. $-11 - |x|$
−15

13. $31 - y - |x|$
24

NAME_____ DATE _____

Study Guide

Rational Numbers

Definition of a Rational Number	A rational number is a number that can be expressed in the form $\frac{a}{b}$, where a and b are integers and $b \neq 0$.

You can compare rational numbers by graphing them on a number line.

Comparing Numbers on the Number Line	If a and b represent any numbers and the graph of a is to the left of the graph of b, then $a < b$. If the graph of a is to the right of the graph of b, then $a > b$.
Comparison Property	For any two numbers a and b, exactly one of the following sentences is true. $a < b$ $a = b$ $a > b$

Example 1: $-3\frac{1}{2} < -\frac{1}{2}$ The graph of $-3\frac{1}{2}$ is to the left of the graph of $-\frac{1}{2}$.

Example 2: $-2\frac{1}{4} > -3\frac{1}{4}$ The graph of $-2\frac{1}{4}$ is to the right of the graph of $-3\frac{1}{4}$.

Example 3: Replace __?__ with $<$, $>$, or $=$ to make the sentence true.
-15 __?__ -3
$-15 \ < \ -3$ Since -15 is to the left of -3 on a number line, -15 is less than -3.

The symbols $\neq$, $\leq$ and $\geq$ can also be used to compare numbers and are called **inequality symbols**.

You can use **cross products** to compare two fractions with different denominators.

Comparison Property for Rational Numbers	For any rational numbers $\frac{a}{b}$ and $\frac{c}{d}$, with $b > 0$ and $d > 0$: 1. if $\frac{a}{b} < \frac{c}{d}$ then $ad < bc$, and 2. if $ad < bc$, then $\frac{a}{b} < \frac{c}{d}$.

This property also holds if $<$ is replaced by $>$, $\leq$, $\geq$, or $=$.

A property that is true for rational numbers but is not true for integers is the **density property**.

Density Property for Rational Numbers	Between every pair of distinct rational numbers, there is another rational number.

Replace each __?__ with <, >, or = to make each sentence true.

1. -4 __?__ 10

2. $\frac{-29}{2}$ __?__ $-28.5 + 14$

3. $-5 - 6$ __?__ $-12 - 1$

Write the numbers in each set in order from least to greatest.

4. $3\frac{1}{3}, \frac{5}{8}, 0.4$

5. $-\frac{3}{2}, \frac{1}{4}, 0.2$

Find a number between the given numbers.

6. $\frac{1}{2}$ and $\frac{7}{9}$

7. $\frac{7}{6}$ and $\frac{9}{8}$

8. $\frac{9}{17}$ and $\frac{2}{5}$

Algebra 1

Rational Numbers

Definition of a Rational Number	A rational number is a number that can be expressed in the form $\frac{a}{b}$, where a and b are integers and $b \neq 0$.

You can compare rational numbers by graphing them on a number line.

Comparing Numbers on the Number Line	If a and b represent any numbers and the graph of a is to the left of the graph of b, then $a < b$. If the graph of a is to the right of the graph of b, then $a > b$.
Comparison Property	For any two numbers a and b, exactly one of the following sentences is true. $a < b$ $a = b$ $a > b$

Example 1: $-3\frac{1}{2} < -\frac{1}{2}$ The graph of $-3\frac{1}{2}$ is to the left of the graph of $-\frac{1}{2}$.

Example 2: $-2\frac{1}{4} > -3\frac{1}{4}$ The graph of $-2\frac{1}{4}$ is to the right of the graph of $-3\frac{1}{4}$.

Example 3: Replace $\underline{\ ?\ }$ with $<$, $>$, or $=$ to make the sentence true.

$$-15 \ \underline{\ ?\ } \ -3$$
$$-15 \ < \ -3 \quad \text{Since } -15 \text{ is to the left of } -3 \text{ on a}$$
number line, -15 is less than -3.

The symbols $\neq$, $\leq$ and $\geq$ can also be used to compare numbers and are called **inequality symbols.**

Comparison Property for Rational Numbers	For any rational numbers $\frac{a}{b}$ and $\frac{c}{d}$, with $b > 0$ and $d > 0$: 1. if $\frac{a}{b} < \frac{c}{d}$ then $ad < bc$, and 2. if $ad < bc$, then $\frac{a}{b} < \frac{c}{d}$.

You can use **cross products** to compare two fractions with different denominators.

This property also holds if $<$ is replaced by $>$, $\leq$, $\geq$, or $=$.

A property that is true for rational numbers but is not true for integers is the **density property.**

Density Property for Rational Numbers	Between every pair of distinct rational numbers, there is another rational number.

Replace each $\underline{\ ?\ }$ with <, >, or = to make each sentence true.

1. $-4 \ \underline{\ ?\ } \ 10$ $<$

2. $\frac{-29}{2} \ \underline{\ ?\ } \ -28.5 + 14$ $=$

3. $-5 - 6 \ \underline{\ ?\ } \ -12 - 1$ $>$

Write the numbers in each set in order from least to greatest.

4. $3\frac{1}{3}, \frac{5}{8}, 0.4$ **$0.4, \frac{5}{8}, 3\frac{1}{3}$**

5. $-\frac{3}{2}, \frac{1}{4}, 0.2$ **$-\frac{3}{2}, 0.2, \frac{1}{4}$**

Find a number between the given numbers.   See students' work.

6. $\frac{1}{2}$ and $\frac{7}{9}$ $\frac{23}{36}$

7. $\frac{7}{6}$ and $\frac{-9}{8}$ $\frac{55}{48}$

8. $\frac{9}{17}$ and $\frac{2}{5}$ $\frac{79}{170}$

NAME_____ DATE _____

Study Guide

Adding and Subtracting Rational Numbers

The rules for adding and subtracting integers also apply to adding and subtracting rational numbers.

Rational Number	Form $\frac{a}{b}$
3	$\frac{3}{1}$
$-2\frac{3}{4}$	$-\frac{11}{4}$
0.125	$\frac{1}{8}$

Example 1: Add $\left(-2\frac{1}{3}\right) + 5\frac{2}{3}$.

$$\left(-2\frac{1}{3}\right) + 5\frac{2}{3} = +\left(\left|5\frac{2}{3}\right| - \left|-2\frac{1}{3}\right|\right)$$
$$= +\left(5\frac{2}{3} - 2\frac{1}{3}\right)$$
$$= 3\frac{1}{3}$$

Example 2: Subtract $-3.42 - 5.82$.
$$-3.42 - 5.82 = -3.42 + (-5.82)$$
$$= -9.24$$

Previously you have added pairs of numbers. To add three or more numbers, first group the numbers in pairs. Use the commutative and associative properties to rearrange the addends if necessary. Study the example at the right.

Example 3: Add $-\frac{2}{3} + \frac{4}{5} + \left(-\frac{5}{3}\right)$.

$$-\frac{2}{3} + \frac{4}{5} + \left(-\frac{5}{3}\right) = \left[-\frac{2}{3} + \left(-\frac{5}{3}\right)\right] + \frac{4}{5}$$
$$= -\frac{7}{3} + \frac{4}{5}$$
$$= -\frac{35}{15} + \frac{12}{15}$$
$$= -\frac{23}{15} \text{ or } -1\frac{8}{15}$$

Find each sum or difference

1. $-\frac{9}{11} + \left(-\frac{13}{11}\right)$

2. $\frac{5}{8} + \left(-\frac{1}{12}\right)$

3. $-0.005 + 0.0043$

4. $\frac{3}{8} - \left(-\frac{1}{8}\right)$

5. $4.59 - 2.31$

6. $-\frac{7}{5} - \frac{2}{7}$

Evaluate each expression if x = −4, y = 3, z = −7.

7. $x + 16$

8. $0 + y$

9. $27 - (x - z)$

10. $100 + (x + y)$

Find each sum.

11. $-36.4 + 29.15 + (-14.2)$ **12.** $6.5x + 12.3x + (-14.9x)$ **13.** $0.85 + 13.6 + (-3.01)$

14. $-9y + (-20y) + 6y$ **15.** $\frac{3}{5} + \left(-\frac{5}{8}\right) + \frac{1}{4}$ **16.** $12p + 11p + (-23p)$

Algebra 1

NAME_____ DATE _____

Study Guide

Adding and Subtracting Rational Numbers

The rules for adding and subtracting integers also apply to adding and subtracting rational numbers.

Rational Number	Form $\frac{a}{b}$
3	$\frac{3}{1}$
$-2\frac{3}{4}$	$-\frac{11}{4}$
0.125	$\frac{1}{8}$

Example 1: Add $\left(-2\frac{1}{3}\right) + 5\frac{2}{3}$.

$$\left(-2\frac{1}{3}\right) + 5\frac{2}{3} = +\left(\left|5\frac{2}{3}\right| - \left|-2\frac{1}{3}\right|\right)$$
$$= +\left(5\frac{2}{3} - 2\frac{1}{3}\right)$$
$$= 3\frac{1}{3}$$

Example 2: Subtract $-3.42 - 5.82$.
$$-3.42 - 5.82 = -3.42 + (-5.82)$$
$$= -9.24$$

Previously you have added pairs of numbers. To add three or more numbers, first group the numbers in pairs. Use the commutative and associative properties to rearrange the addends if necessary. Study the example at the right.

Example 3: Add $-\frac{2}{3} + \frac{4}{5} + \left(-\frac{5}{3}\right)$.

$$-\frac{2}{3} + \frac{4}{5} + \left(-\frac{5}{3}\right) = \left[-\frac{2}{3} + \left(-\frac{5}{3}\right)\right] + \frac{4}{5}$$
$$= -\frac{7}{3} + \frac{4}{5}$$
$$= -\frac{35}{15} + \frac{12}{15}$$
$$= -\frac{23}{15} \text{ or } -1\frac{8}{15}$$

Find each sum or difference

1. $-\frac{9}{11} + \left(-\frac{13}{11}\right)$ **−2**

2. $\frac{5}{8} + \left(-\frac{1}{12}\right)$ **$\frac{13}{24}$**

3. $-0.005 + 0.0043$ **−0.0007**

4. $\frac{3}{8} - \left(-\frac{1}{8}\right)$ **$\frac{1}{2}$**

5. $4.59 - 2.31$ **2.28**

6. $-\frac{7}{5} - \frac{2}{7}$ **$-\frac{59}{35}$**

Evaluate each expression if x = −4, y = 3, z = −7.

7. $x + 16$ **12**

8. $0 + y$ **3**

9. $27 - (x - z)$ **24**

10. $100 + (x + y)$ **99**

Find each sum.

11. $-36.4 + 29.15 + (-14.2)$ **−21.45**

12. $6.5x + 12.3x + (-14.9x)$ **3.9x**

13. $0.85 + 13.6 + (-3.01)$ **11.44**

14. $-9y + (-20y) + 6y$ **−23y**

15. $\frac{3}{5} + \left(-\frac{5}{8}\right) + \frac{1}{4}$ **$\frac{9}{40}$**

16. $12p + 11p + (-23p)$ **0**

2-6

Study Guide

Multiplying Rational Numbers

You can use the rules below when multiplying rational numbers.

Rule or Property		Example
Multiplying Two Numbers with Different Signs	The product of two numbers that have different signs is negative.	$(-2x)5y = (-2)(5)xy$ $= -10xy$
Multiplying Two Numbers with the Same Sign	The product of two numbers that have the same sign is positive.	$(-4)(-7) = 28$
Multiplicative Property of -1	The product of any number and -1 is its additive inverse. $-1(a) = -a$ and $a(-1) = -a$	$(-3)(-4)(-1)(2) = 12(-1)(2)$ $= -12(2)$ $= -24$

To find the product of two or more numbers, first group the numbers in pairs.

Example: Multiply $(-2.3)(5.6)(-0.7)(-0.2)$

$$(-2.3)(5.6)(-0.7)(-0.2) = [(-2.3)(5.6)][(-0.7)(-0.2)] \quad \textbf{Associative property } (\times)$$
$$= (-12.88)(0.14) \quad \textbf{Substitution property } (=)$$
$$= -1.8032$$

Find each product.

1. $(-24)(-2)$

2. $(6.0)(-0.3)$

3. $(-2)(-3)(-4)$

4. $\left(\frac{1}{2}\right)(-10)(5)$

5. $(-22)(-3)\left(-\frac{2}{3}\right)$

6. $\left(\frac{4}{5}\right)(-5)(0)(4)$

Simplify.

7. $(-6)(5) + (2)(4)$

8. $\left(-\frac{3}{4}\right)\left(\frac{1}{8}\right) - \left(\frac{1}{4}\right)\left(\frac{1}{8}\right)$

9. $-5(2x + x) - 3(-xy)$

10. $(-5ab)6 - ab(4 + 1)$

11. $2.3(4c - d) - 0.1(-0.5c + 8d)$

12. $(-0.9)(1.1) - (-5.1)(0.6)$

NAME_____ DATE _____

Study Guide

Multiplying Rational Numbers

You can use the rules below when multiplying rational numbers.

Rule or Property		Example
Multiplying Two Numbers with Different Signs	The product of two numbers that have different signs is negative.	$(-2x)5y = (-2)(5)xy$ $= -10xy$
Multiplying Two Numbers with the Same Sign	The product of two numbers that have the same sign is positive.	$(-4)(-7) = 28$
Multiplicative Property of -1	The product of any number and -1 is its additive inverse. $-1(a) = -a$ and $a(-1) = -a$	$(-3)(-4)(-1)(2) = 12(-1)(2)$ $= -12(2)$ $= -24$

To find the product of two or more numbers, first group the numbers in pairs.

Example: Multiply $(-2.3)(5.6)(-0.7)(-0.2)$

$\qquad (-2.3)(5.6)(-0.7)(-0.2) = [(-2.3)(5.6)][(-0.7)(-0.2)]$ **Associative property (×)**
$\qquad\qquad\qquad\qquad\qquad = (-12.88)(0.14)$ **Substitution property (=)**
$\qquad\qquad\qquad\qquad\qquad = -1.8032$

Find each product.

1. $(-24)(-2)$ **48**

2. $(6.0)(-0.3)$ **−1.8**

3. $(-2)(-3)(-4)$ **−24**

4. $\left(\frac{1}{2}\right)(-10)(5)$ **−25**

5. $(-22)(-3)\left(-\frac{2}{3}\right)$ **−44**

6. $\left(\frac{4}{5}\right)(-5)(0)(4)$ **0**

Simplify.

7. $(-6)(5) + (2)(4)$ **−22**

8. $\left(-\frac{3}{4}\right)\left(\frac{1}{8}\right) - \left(\frac{1}{4}\right)\left(\frac{1}{8}\right)$ **$-\frac{1}{8}$**

9. $-5(2x + x) - 3(-xy)$
$\quad$ **−15x + 3xy**

10. $(-5ab)6 - ab(4 + 1)$ **−35ab**

11. $2.3(4c - d) - 0.1(-0.5c + 8d)$
$\quad$ **9.25c − 3.1d**

12. $(-0.9)(1.1) - (-5.1)(0.6)$ **2.07**

Algebra 1

Dividing Rational Numbers

Use the following rules to divide rational numbers.

Rule or Property		Example
Dividing Rational Numbers	The quotient of two numbers is positive if the numbers have the same sign. The quotient of two numbers is negative if the numbers have different signs.	$-60 \div (-10) = 6$ $-48 \div 4 = -12$
Multiplicative Inverse Property	For every nonzero number a, there is exactly one number $\frac{1}{a}$, such that $(a)\frac{1}{a} = \frac{1}{a}(a) = 1$.	$\frac{1}{3} \div \frac{3}{4} = \frac{1}{3} \cdot \frac{4}{3}$ $= \frac{4}{9}$
Division Rule	For all numbers a and b, with $b \neq 0$, $a \div b = \frac{a}{b} = a\left(\frac{1}{b}\right) = \frac{1}{b}(a)$.	$6 \div 2 = \frac{6}{2}$ $= (6)\frac{1}{2}$ $= \frac{1}{2}(6) = 3$

Since the fraction bar indicates division, you can use the division rules and the distributive property to simplify rational expressions.

Example: Simplify $\dfrac{-20a + 15}{5}$.

$$\frac{-20a + 15}{5} = (-20a + 15)\left(\frac{1}{5}\right)$$
$$= (-20a)\left(\frac{1}{5}\right) + (15)\left(\frac{1}{5}\right)$$
$$= -4a + 3$$

Simplify.

1. $\dfrac{-44a}{4}$

2. $\dfrac{16x}{2}$

3. $\dfrac{80}{5}$

4. $\dfrac{81}{-27}$

5. $\dfrac{-144a}{6}$

6. $\dfrac{-30}{-10} \div \dfrac{30}{10}$

7. $\dfrac{57y}{3}$

8. $-\dfrac{1}{2} \div 8$

9. $\dfrac{18a - 6b}{-3}$

10. $\dfrac{12x}{3} \div \dfrac{1}{12} + xyz$

11. $\dfrac{36a - 12}{12}$

12. $\dfrac{-\frac{5}{8}}{5}$

Study Guide

Dividing Rational Numbers

Use the following rules to divide rational numbers.

Rule or Property		Example
Dividing Rational Numbers	The quotient of two numbers is positive if the numbers have the same sign. The quotient of two numbers is negative if the numbers have different signs.	$-60 \div (-10) = 6$ $-48 \div 4 = -12$
Multiplicative Inverse Property	For every nonzero number a, there is exactly one number $\frac{1}{a}$, such that $(a)\frac{1}{a} = \frac{1}{a}(a) = 1$.	$\frac{1}{3} \div \frac{3}{4} = \frac{1}{3} \cdot \frac{4}{3}$ $= \frac{4}{9}$
Division Rule	For all numbers a and b, with $b \neq 0$, $a \div b = \frac{a}{b} = a\left(\frac{1}{b}\right) = \frac{1}{b}(a)$.	$6 \div 2 = \frac{6}{2}$ $= (6)\frac{1}{2}$ $= \frac{1}{2}(6) = 3$

Since the fraction bar indicates division, you can use the division rules and the distributive property to simplify rational expressions.

Example: Simplify $\dfrac{-20a + 15}{5}$.

$$\frac{-20a + 15}{5} = (-20a + 15)\left(\frac{1}{5}\right)$$
$$= (-20a)\left(\frac{1}{5}\right) + (15)\left(\frac{1}{5}\right)$$
$$= -4a + 3$$

Simplify.

1. $\dfrac{-44a}{4}$ **−11a**

2. $\dfrac{16x}{2}$ **8x**

3. $\dfrac{80}{5}$ **16**

4. $\dfrac{81}{-27}$ **−3**

5. $\dfrac{-144a}{6}$ **−24a**

6. $\dfrac{-30}{-10} \div \dfrac{30}{10}$ **1**

7. $\dfrac{57y}{3}$ **19y**

8. $-\dfrac{1}{2} \div 8$ **$-\dfrac{1}{16}$**

9. $\dfrac{18a - 6b}{-3}$ **−6a + 2b**

10. $\dfrac{12x}{3} \div \dfrac{1}{12} + xyz$ **48x + xyz**

11. $\dfrac{36a - 12}{12}$ **3a − 1**

12. $\dfrac{-\frac{5}{8}}{5}$ **$-\dfrac{1}{8}$**

NAME _____ DATE _____

Study Guide

Square Roots and Real Numbers

The chart below illustrates the various kinds of real numbers.

Counting or Natural Numbers, N	$\{1, 2, 3, 4, \cdots\}$
Whole Numbers, W	$\{0, 1, 2, 3, 4, \cdots\}$
Integers, Z	$\{\cdots -3, -2, -1, 0, 1, 2, 3, \cdots\}$
Rational Numbers, Q	$\left\{ \text{all numbers that can be expressed in the form} \atop \frac{a}{b}, \text{ where } a \text{ and } b \text{ are integers and } b \neq 0 \right\}$
Irrational Numbers, I	$\left\{ \text{numbers that cannot be expressed in the form} \atop \frac{a}{b}, \text{ where } a \text{ and } b \text{ are integers and } b \neq 0 \right\}$
Real Numbers, R	{rational numbers and irrational numbers}

The square roots of perfect squares are classified as rational numbers. A **square root** is one of two equal factors of a number. For example, the square root of 36 is 6 and -6 since $6 \cdot 6$ or 6^2 is 36 and $(-6)(-6)$ or $(-6)^2$ is also 36. A rational number like 36, whose square root is a rational number, is called a **perfect square.**

The symbol $\sqrt{}$ is called a **radical sign.** It indicates the nonnegative, or **principal,** square root of the expression under the radical sign.

Example: Find $\pm\sqrt{49}$.   The symbol $\pm\sqrt{49}$ represents both square roots. Since $7^2 = 49$, we know that $\pm\sqrt{49} = \pm 7$.

Numbers such as $\sqrt{2}$ and $\sqrt{3}$ are not perfect squares. Notice what happens when you find these square roots with your calculator. The numbers continue indefinitely without any pattern of repeating digits. These numbers are not rational numbers since they are not repeating or terminating decimals and they are classified as **irrational numbers.**

Find each square root. Use a calculator if necessary. Round to the nearest hundredth if the result is not a whole number or simple fraction.

1. $\sqrt{81}$ 2. $\sqrt{0.00025}$ 3. $-\sqrt{\dfrac{25}{16}}$ 4. $-\sqrt{3600}$ 5. $\pm\sqrt{\dfrac{121}{100}}$

Evaluate each expression. Use a calculator if necessary. Round to the nearest hundredth if the result is not a whole number.

6. $\sqrt{a}$, if $a = 39$

7. $\pm\sqrt{s + t}$, if $s = 30$ and $t = 19$

8. $-\sqrt{\dfrac{a}{b}}$, if $a = 169$ and $b = 4$

9. $\sqrt{cd}$, if $c = 12$ and $d = 15$

Name the set or sets of numbers to which each real number belongs. Use N for natural numbers, W for whole numbers, Z for integers, Q for rational numbers, and I for irrational numbers.

10. 3.145

11. $\sqrt{11}$

12. $\sqrt{25}$

Study Guide

Square Roots and Real Numbers

The chart below illustrates the various kinds of real numbers.

Counting or Natural Numbers, N	{1, 2, 3, 4, ⋯}
Whole Numbers, W	{0, 1, 2, 3, 4, ⋯}
Integers, Z	{⋯ −3, −2, −1, 0, 1, 2, 3, ⋯}
Rational Numbers, Q	{all numbers that can be expressed in the form $\frac{a}{b}$, where a and b are integers and $b \neq 0$}
Irrational Numbers, I	{numbers that cannot be expressed in the form $\frac{a}{b}$, where a and b are integers and $b \neq 0$}
Real Numbers, R	{rational numbers and irrational numbers}

The square roots of perfect squares are classified as rational numbers. A **square root** is one of two equal factors of a number. For example, the square root of 36 is 6 and −6 since 6 · 6 or 6² is 36 and (−6)(−6) or (−6)² is also 36. A rational number like 36, whose square root is a rational number, is called a **perfect square.**

The symbol $\sqrt{}$ is called a **radical sign.** It indicates the nonnegative, or **principal,** square root of the expression under the radical sign.

Example: Find $\pm\sqrt{49}$.   The symbol $\pm\sqrt{49}$ represents both square roots. Since 7² = 49, we know that $\pm\sqrt{49} = \pm 7$.

Numbers such as $\sqrt{2}$ and $\sqrt{3}$ are not perfect squares. Notice what happens when you find these square roots with your calculator. The numbers continue indefinitely without any pattern of repeating digits. These numbers are not rational numbers since they are not repeating or terminating decimals and they are classified as **irrational numbers.**

Find each square root. Use a calculator if necessary. Round to the nearest hundredth if the result is not a whole number or simple fraction.

1. $\sqrt{81}$ **9**

2. $\sqrt{0.00025}$ **0.02**

3. $-\sqrt{\frac{25}{16}}$ $-\frac{5}{4}$

4. $-\sqrt{3600}$ **−60**

5. $\pm\sqrt{\frac{121}{100}}$ $\pm\frac{11}{10}$

Evaluate each expression. Use a calculator if necessary. Round to the nearest hundredth if the result is not a whole number.

6. $\sqrt{a}$, if $a = 39$ **6.24**

7. $\pm\sqrt{s + t}$, if $s = 30$ and $t = 19$ **±7**

8. $-\sqrt{\frac{a}{b}}$, if $a = 169$ and $b = 4$ $-\frac{13}{2}$

9. $\sqrt{cd}$, if $c = 12$ and $d = 15$ **13.42**

Name the set or sets of numbers to which each real number belongs. Use N for natural numbers, W for whole numbers, Z for integers, Q for rational numbers, and I for irrational numbers.

10. 3.145 **Q**

11. $\sqrt{11}$ **I**

12. $\sqrt{25}$ **Z; Q**

 Algebra 1

NAME_____ DATE _____

Study Guide

Problem Solving
Write Equations and Formulas

When solving a problem, you should read and explore the problem until you completely understand the relationships in the given information. Then you may translate the problem into an equation or formula. In an equation, you choose a variable to represent one of the unspecified numbers in the problem. This is called **defining the variable.** Then use the variable to write expressions for the other unspecified numbers in the problem. In a formula, an equation that states a rule for the relationship between certain quantities is formed.

Problem-Solving Plan
1. Explore the problem.
2. Plan the solution.
3. Solve the problem.
4. Examine the solution.

Example: Find the area of a rectangle with length 15 cm and width 12 cm. Use the formula $A = \ell w$.

$A = \ell w$
$A = 15 \cdot 12$
$A = 180$ The area of the rectangle is 180 cm².

Answer the related questions for the verbal problems below.

1. Kevin can mow a lawn in 2 hours. Kelley can mow the same lawn in 4 hours.
   a. How much of the lawn can Kevin mow in one hour?
   b. How much of the lawn can Kelley mow in one hour?

2. A bus can hold a maximum of 70 people. The bus is four-fifths full. Three-fourths of the people on the bus get off at the first stop.
   a. How many people are on the bus before the first stop?
   b. How many people get off the bus at the first stop?

Translate each sentence into an equation, an inequality or formula.

3. The area A of a circle is the product of π and the radius r squared.

4. One-half of the difference of a and b is 54.

5. The product of a and b is less than five times the difference of a and b.

Define a variable, then write an equation for each problem. Do not try to solve.

6. One number is 50 less than a second number. The sum of the two is 108. Find the numbers.

7. Pete has 20 pets. If he has 5 more than $\frac{1}{4}$ as many dogs as cats, how many cats does Pete have?

Problem Solving
Write Equations and Formulas

When solving a problem, you should read and explore the problem until you completely understand the relationships in the given information. Then you may translate the problem into an equation or formula. In an equation, you choose a variable to represent one of the unspecified numbers in the problem. This is called **defining the variable.** Then use the variable to write expressions for the other unspecified numbers in the problem. In a formula, an equation that states a rule for the relationship between certain quantities is formed.

Problem-Solving Plan
1. Explore the problem.
2. Plan the solution.
3. Solve the problem.
4. Examine the solution.

Example: Find the area of a rectangle with length 15 cm and width 12 cm. Use the formula $A = \ell w$.

$A = \ell w$
$A = 15 \cdot 12$
$A = 180$ The area of the rectangle is 180 cm².

Answer the related questions for the verbal problems below.

1. Kevin can mow a lawn in 2 hours. Kelley can mow the same lawn in 4 hours.
   a. How much of the lawn can Kevin mow in one hour? $\frac{1}{2}$
   b. How much of the lawn can Kelley mow in one hour? $\frac{1}{4}$

2. A bus can hold a maximum of 70 people. The bus is four-fifths full. Three-fourths of the people on the bus get off at the first stop.
   a. How many people are on the bus before the first stop? **56**
   b. How many people get off the bus at the first stop? **42**

Translate each sentence into an equation, an inequality or formula.

3. The area A of a circle is the product of π and the radius r squared. $A = \pi r^2$

4. One-half of the difference of a and b is 54. $\frac{1}{2}(a - b) = 54$

5. The product of a and b is less than five times the difference of a and b. $ab < 5(a - b)$

Define a variable, then write an equation for each problem.
Do not try to solve.

6. One number is 50 less than a second number. The sum of the two is 108. Find the numbers. **Let x = one number, then $x - 50$ = the other number. So the equation is $x + (x - 50) = 108$.**

7. Pete has 20 pets. If he has 5 more than $\frac{1}{4}$ as many dogs as cats, how many cats does Pete have? **Let x = the number of dogs, then $\frac{1}{4}x + 5$ = the number of cats. So the equation is $x + \frac{1}{4}x + 5 = 20$.**

3-1

Study Guide

Solving Equations with Addition and Subtraction

You can use the addition and subtraction properties of equality to solve equations. To check, substitute the solution for the variable in the original equation. If the resulting sentence is true, your solution is correct.

Addition Property of Equality	For any numbers a, b, and c, if $a = b$, then $a + c = b + c$.
Subtraction Property of Equality	For any numbers a, b, and c, if $a = b$, then $a - c = b - c$.

Example 1: Solve $r - 6 = -11$.

$$r - 6 = -11$$
$$r - 6 + 6 = -11 + 6$$
$$r = -5$$

Check:
$$r - 6 = -11$$
$$-5 - 6 = -11$$
$$-11 = -11 \checkmark$$

Example 2: Solve $k + 18 = -9$.

$$k + 18 = -9$$
$$k + 18 - 18 = -9 - 18$$
$$k = -27$$

Check:
$$k + 18 = -9$$
$$-27 + 18 = -9$$
$$-9 = -9 \checkmark$$

Sometimes an equation can be solved more easily if it is rewritten first. Recall that subtracting a number is the same as adding its inverse. For example, the equation $g - (-5) = 18$ may be rewritten as $g + 5 = 18$.

Solve each equation. Then check your solution.

1. $b - 17 = -40$

2. $x + 12 = 6$

3. $z + 2 = -13$

4. $-17 = b + 4$

5. $s + (-9) = 7$

6. $v - (-12) = 10$

7. $19 + h = -4$

8. $73 = 29 - q$

9. $-3.2 = l + (-0.2)$

10. $-25 - r = \dfrac{4}{36}$

11. $-\dfrac{3}{8} + x = \dfrac{5}{8}$

12. $\dfrac{5}{9} = -y + \dfrac{2}{15}$

Algebra 1

Study Guide

Solving Equations with Addition and Subtraction

You can use the addition and subtraction properties of equality to solve equations. To check, substitute the solution for the variable in the original equation. If the resulting sentence is true, your solution is correct.

Addition Property of Equality	For any numbers a, b, and c, if $a = b$, then $a + c = b + c$.
Subtraction Property of Equality	For any numbers a, b, and c, if $a = b$, then $a - c = b - c$.

Example 1: Solve $r - 6 = -11$.

$$r - 6 = -11$$
$$r - 6 + 6 = -11 + 6$$
$$r = -5$$

Check:
$$r - 6 = -11$$
$$-5 - 6 = -11$$
$$-11 = -11 ✔$$

Example 2: Solve $k + 18 = -9$.

$$k + 18 = -9$$
$$k + 18 - 18 = -9 - 18$$
$$k = -27$$

Check:
$$k + 18 = -9$$
$$-27 + 18 = -9$$
$$-9 = -9 ✔$$

Sometimes an equation can be solved more easily if it is rewritten first. Recall that subtracting a number is the same as adding its inverse. For example, the equation $g - (-5) = 18$ may be rewritten as $g + 5 = 18$.

Solve each equation. Then check your solution.

1. $b - 17 = -40$ **−23**

2. $x + 12 = 6$ **−6**

3. $z + 2 = -13$ **−15**

4. $-17 = b + 4$ **−21**

5. $s + (-9) = 7$ **16**

6. $v - (-12) = 10$ **−2**

7. $19 + h = -4$ **−23**

8. $73 = 29 - q$ **−44**

9. $-3.2 = l + (-0.2)$ **−3**

10. $-25 - r = \frac{4}{36}$ **$-25\frac{1}{9}$**

11. $-\frac{3}{8} + x = \frac{5}{8}$ **1**

12. $\frac{5}{9} = -y + \frac{2}{15}$ **$-\frac{19}{45}$**

Study Guide

Solving Equations with Multiplication and Division

You can solve equations in which a variable has a coefficient by using the multiplication and division properties of equality.

Multiplicative Property of Equality	For any numbers a, b, and c, with $c \neq 0$, if $a = b$, then $ac = bc$.
Division Property of Equality	For any numbers a, b, and c, with $c \neq 0$, if $a = b$, then $\dfrac{a}{c} = \dfrac{b}{c}$.

Example 1: Solve $\frac{1}{4}n = 16$.

$$\frac{1}{4}n = 16$$
$$4\left(\frac{1}{4}n\right) = 4(16)$$
$$n = 64$$

Check: $\frac{1}{4}n = 16$

$$\frac{1}{4}(64) \stackrel{?}{=} 16$$
$$16 = 16 \checkmark$$

Example 2: Solve $8n = 64$.

$$8n = 64$$
$$\frac{8n}{8} = \frac{64}{8}$$
$$n = 8$$

Check: $8n = 64$

$$8(8) \stackrel{?}{=} 64$$
$$64 = 64 \checkmark$$

Solve each equation. Then check your solution.

1. $-3r = -24$
2. $8s = -64$
3. $-3t = 51$
4. $\frac{1}{4}w = -16$
5. $6x = \frac{3}{4}$
6. $1\frac{1}{4}y = -3\frac{3}{4}$

Define a variable, write an equation, and solve each problem. Then check your solution.

7. Twelve times a number is 96. What is the number?

8. One half of a number is fifteen. What is the number?

9. Negative four times a number is -112. What is the number?

10. Regina paid \$53.50 for 5 basketball tickets. What is the cost of each ticket?

Complete.

11. If $4x = 100$, then $8x =$ _____.

12. If $6y = 36$, then $3y =$ _____.

13. If $-10a = 53$, then $-5a =$ _____.

14. If $2g + h = 12$, then $4g + 2h =$ _____.

Solving Equations with Multiplication and Division

You can solve equations in which a variable has a coefficient by using the multiplication and division properties of equality.

Multiplicative Property of Equality	For any numbers a, b, and c, with $c \neq 0$, if $a = b$, then $ac = bc$.
Division Property of Equality	For any numbers a, b, and c, with $c \neq 0$, if $a = b$, then $\dfrac{a}{c} = \dfrac{b}{c}$.

Example 1: Solve $\frac{1}{4}n = 16$.

$$\frac{1}{4}n = 16$$

$$4\left(\frac{1}{4}n\right) = 4(16)$$

$$n = 64$$

Check: $\frac{1}{4}n = 16$

$$\frac{1}{4}(64) \stackrel{?}{=} 16$$

$$16 = 16 ✔$$

Example 2: Solve $8n = 64$.

$$8n = 64$$

$$\frac{8n}{8} = \frac{64}{8}$$

$$n = 8$$

Check: $8n = 64$

$$8(8) \stackrel{?}{=} 64$$

$$64 = 64 ✔$$

Solve each equation. Then check your solution.

1. $-3r = -24$ **8**

2. $8s = -64$ **−8**

3. $-3t = 51$ **−17**

4. $\frac{1}{4}w = -16$ **−64**

5. $6x = \frac{3}{4}$ **$\frac{1}{8}$**

6. $1\frac{1}{4}y = -3\frac{3}{4}$ **−3**

Define a variable, write an equation, and solve each problem. Then check your solution.

7. Twelve times a number is 96. What is the number? **$12n = 96$; 8**

8. One half of a number is fifteen. What is the number? **$\frac{1}{2}n = 15$; 30**

9. Negative four times a number is -112. What is the number? **$-4n = -112$; 28**

10. Regina paid $53.50 for 5 basketball tickets. What is the cost of each ticket? **$5t = 53.50$; $10.70**

Complete.

11. If $4x = 100$, then $8x = $ ___**200**___.

12. If $6y = 36$, then $3y = $ ___**18**___.

13. If $-10a = 53$, then $-5a = $ ___**26.5**___.

14. If $2g + h = 12$, then $4g + 2h = $ ___**24**___.

3-3

Study Guide

Solving Multi-Step Equations

When solving some equations you must perform more than one operation on both sides. First, determine what operations have been done to the variable. Then undo these operations in the reverse order.

Example 1: How would you solve $\frac{n}{3} - 7 = 28$?

$$\frac{n}{3} - 7 = 28$$

First, n was divided by 3. \
Then 7 was subtracted. } To solve, first add 7 to each side. \
Then multiply each side by 3.

Procedure for Solving a Two-Step Equation	1. Undo any indicated additions or subtractions. 2. Undo any indicated multiplications or divisions involving the variable.

Example 2: $5x + 3 = 23$ Addition of 3 is indicated.

$5x + 3 - 3 = 23 - 3$ Therefore, subtract 3 from each side.

$5x = 20$ Multiplication by 5 is also indicated.

$\frac{5x}{5} = \frac{20}{5}$ Therefore, divide each side by 5.

$x = 4$

Check:
$5x + 3 = 23$
$5(4) + 3 \stackrel{?}{=} 23$
$20 + 3 \stackrel{?}{=} 23$
$23 = 23$ ✔

Solve each equation. Then check your solution.

1. $5z + 16 = 51$

2. $14n - 8 = 34$

3. $0.6x - 1.5 = 1.8$

4. $\frac{4b + 8}{-2} = 10$

5. $16 = \frac{d - 12}{14}$

6. $8 + \frac{3n}{12} = 13$

7. $\frac{7}{8}p - 4 = 10$

8. $\frac{g}{-5} + 3 = -13$

9. $-4 = \frac{7x - (-1)}{-8}$

Define a variable, write an equation, and solve each problem. Then check your solution.

10. Find three consecutive integers whose sum is 96.

11. Find two consecutive odd integers whose sum is 176.

Study Guide

Solving Multi-Step Equations

When solving some equations you must perform more than one operation on both sides. First, determine what operations have been done to the variable. Then undo these operations in the reverse order.

Example 1: How would you solve $\frac{n}{3} - 7 = 28$?

$$\frac{n}{3} - 7 = 28$$

First, n was divided by 3. } To solve, first add 7 to each side.
Then 7 was subtracted. } Then multiply each side by 3.

Procedure for Solving a Two-Step Equation	1. Undo any indicated additions or subtractions. 2. Undo any indicated multiplications or divisions involving the variable.

Example 2: $5x + 3 = 23$ Addition of 3 is indicated.

Check:
$$5x + 3 = 23$$

$5x + 3 - 3 = 23 - 3$ Therefore, subtract 3 from each side. $5(4) + 3 \stackrel{?}{=} 23$

$5x = 20$ Multiplication by 5 is also indicated. $20 + 3 \stackrel{?}{=} 23$

$\frac{5x}{5} = \frac{20}{5}$ Therefore, divide each side by 5. $23 = 23$ ✔

$x = 4$

Solve each equation. Then check your solution.

1. $5z + 16 = 51$ **7**

2. $14n - 8 = 34$ **3**

3. $0.6x - 1.5 = 1.8$ **5.5**

4. $\frac{4b + 8}{-2} = 10$ **−7**

5. $16 = \frac{d - 12}{14}$ **236**

6. $8 + \frac{3n}{12} = 13$ **20**

7. $\frac{7}{8}p - 4 = 10$ **16**

8. $\frac{g}{-5} + 3 = -13$ **80**

9. $-4 = \frac{7x - (-1)}{-8}$ $\frac{31}{7}$**, or** $4\frac{3}{7}$

Define a variable, write an equation, and solve each problem. Then check your solution.

10. Find three consecutive integers whose sum is 96.
$n + (n + 1) + (n + 2) = 96$; **31, 32, 33**

11. Find two consecutive odd integers whose sum is 176.
$n + (n + 2) = 176$; **87, 89**

Study Guide

Integration: Geometry
Angles and Triangles

Supplementary Angles	Two angles are supplementary if the sum of their measures is 180°.
Complementary Angles	Two angles are complementary if the sum of their measures is 90°.
Sum of the Angles of a Triangle	The sum of the measures of the angles in any triangle is 180°.

Example 1: The measure of an angle is twice the measure of its complement. Find the measure of each angle.

Let x = the lesser measure. Then $2x$ = the greater measure.

$x + 2x = 90$ **The sum of the measures is 90°.**

$3x = 90$ **Add x and $2x$.**

$\dfrac{3x}{3} = \dfrac{90}{3}$ **Divide each side by 3.**

$x = 30$ The measures are 30° and $2 \cdot 30$° or 60°.

Example 2: The measures of two angles of a triangle are 26° and 77°. Find the measure of the third angle.

Let x = the measure of the third angle.

$26 + 77 + x = 180$ **The sum of the measures of the angles is 180°.**

$103 + x = 180$ **Add 26 and 77.**

$103 - 103 + x = 180 - 103$ **Subtract 103 from each side.**

$x = 77$ The measure of the third angle is 77°.

Find both the complement and the supplement of each angle measure.

1. 39°

2. 85°

3. 13°

4. t°

5. $(a - 6)$°

6. $(35 - x)$°

Find the measure of the third angle of each triangle in which the measures of two angles of the triangle are given.

7. 120°, 45°

8. 55°, 55°

9. $t, 3t$

Write an equation and solve. Then check your solution.

10. The measure of an angle is 74° greater than its supplement. Find the measure of each angle.

11. One of two complementary angles is 24° more than twice the other. Find the measure of each angle.

Study Guide

Integration: Geometry
Angles and Triangles

Supplementary Angles	Two angles are supplementary if the sum of their measures is 180°.
Complementary Angles	Two angles are complementary if the sum of their measures is 90°.
Sum of the Angles of a Triangle	The sum of the measures of the angles in any triangle is 180°.

Example 1: The measure of an angle is twice the measure of its complement. Find the measure of each angle.

Let x = the lesser measure. Then $2x$ = the greater measure.

$x + 2x = 90$	**The sum of the measures is 90°.**
$3x = 90$	**Add x and $2x$.**
$\dfrac{3x}{3} = \dfrac{90}{3}$	**Divide each side by 3.**
$x = 30$	The measures are 30° and $2 \cdot 30°$ or 60°.

Example 2: The measures of two angles of a triangle are 26° and 77°. Find the measure of the third angle.

Let x = the measure of the third angle.

$26 + 77 + x = 180$	**The sum of the measures of the angles is 180°.**
$103 + x = 180$	**Add 26 and 77.**
$103 - 103 + x = 180 - 103$	**Subtract 103 from each side.**
$x = 77$	The measure of the third angle is 77°.

Find both the complement and the supplement of each angle measure.

1. 39° **51°; 141°**

2. 85° **5°; 95°**

3. 13° **77°; 167°**

4. $t°$
   $(90 - t)°$; $(180 - t)°$

5. $(a - 6)°$
   $(96 - a)°$; $(186 - a)°$

6. $(35 - x)°$
   $(55 + x)°$; $(145 + x)°$

Find the measure of the third angle of each triangle in which the measures of two angles of the triangle are given.

7. 120°, 45° **15°**

8. 55°, 55° **70°**

9. t, $3t$ **$(180 - 4t)°$**

Write an equation and solve. Then check your solution.

10. The measure of an angle is 74° greater than its supplement. Find the measure of each angle. **53°, 127°**

11. One of two complementary angles is 24° more than twice the other. Find the measure of each angle. **22°, 68°**

Study Guide

Solving Equations with the Variable on Both Sides

When an equation contains parentheses or other grouping symbols, first use the distributive property to remove the grouping symbols. If the equation has variables on each side, use addition and subtraction property of equality to write an equivalent equation that has all the variables on one side. Then solve the equation.

Example: Solve $4(2a - 1) = -10(a - 5)$.

$$4(2a - 1) = -10(a - 5)$$

$$8a - 4 = -10a + 50 \qquad \text{Use the distributive property.}$$

$$8a + 10a - 4 = -10a + 10a + 50 \qquad \text{Add 10a to each side.}$$

$$18a - 4 = 50$$

$$18a - 4 + 4 = 50 + 4 \qquad \text{Add 4 to each side.}$$

$$18a = 54$$

$$\frac{18a}{18} = \frac{54}{18} \qquad \text{Divide each side by 18.}$$

$$a = 3$$

Check:

$$4(2a - 1) = -10(a - 5)$$
$$4(2 \cdot 3 - 1) = -10(3 - 5)$$
$$4(6 - 1) = -10(-2)$$
$$4(5) = -10(-2)$$
$$20 = 20 \; ✔$$

Some equations may have *no solution,* and some equations may have *every number* in their solution set. An equation that is true for every value of the variable is called an **identity.**

Solve each equation. Then check your solution.

1. $-3(x + 5) = 3(x - 1)$ **2.** $6 - b = 5b + 30$ **3.** $5y - 2y = 3y + 2$

4. $2(7 + 3t) = -t$ **5.** $3(a + 1) - 5 = 3a - 2$ **6.** $75 - 9g = 5(-4 + 2g)$

7. $1.2x + 4.3 = 2.1 - x$ **8.** $4.4s + 6.2 = 8.8s - 1.8$ **9.** $5(f + 2) = 2(3 - f)$

10. $\frac{1}{2}b + 4 = \frac{1}{8}b + 88$ **11.** $\frac{2}{5}w - w = -\frac{1}{5}(3w + 2)$ **12.** $5(p + 3) + 9 = 3(p - 2) + 6$

13. $\frac{3}{4}k - 5 = \frac{1}{4}k - 1$ **14.** $0.03g - (2g + 3) = 1.8$ **15.** $-5(2r + 3) = 3(11 - 4r) - 58$

Solving Equations with the Variable on Both Sides

When an equation contains parentheses or other grouping symbols, first use the distributive property to remove the grouping symbols. If the equation has variables on each side, use addition and subtraction property of equality to write an equivalent equation that has all the variables on one side. Then solve the equation.

Example: Solve $4(2a - 1) = -10(a - 5)$.

$$4(2a - 1) = -10(a - 5)$$
$$8a - 4 = -10a + 50 \qquad \text{Use the distributive property.}$$
$$8a + 10a - 4 = -10a + 10a + 50 \qquad \text{Add 10}a \text{ to each side.}$$
$$18a - 4 = 50$$
$$18a - 4 + 4 = 50 + 4 \qquad \text{Add 4 to each side.}$$
$$18a = 54$$
$$\frac{18a}{18} = \frac{54}{18} \qquad \text{Divide each side by 18.}$$
$$a = 3$$

Check:
$$4(2a - 1) = -10(a - 5)$$
$$4(2 \cdot 3 - 1) = -10(3 - 5)$$
$$4(6 - 1) = -10(-2)$$
$$4(5) = -10(-2)$$
$$20 = 20 \; ✔$$

Some equations may have *no solution,* and some equations may have *every number* in their solution set. An equation that is true for every value of the variable is called an **identity**.

Solve each equation. Then check your solution.

1. $-3(x + 5) = 3(x - 1)$
−2

2. $6 - b = 5b + 30$
−4

3. $5y - 2y = 3y + 2$
no solution

4. $2(7 + 3t) = -t$
−2

5. $3(a + 1) -5 = 3a - 2$
identity

6. $75 - 9g = 5(-4 + 2g)$
5

7. $1.2x + 4.3 = 2.1 - x$
−1

8. $4.4s + 6.2 = 8.8s - 1.8$
$\dfrac{20}{11}$

9. $5(f + 2) = 2(3 - f)$
$-\dfrac{4}{7}$

10. $\frac{1}{2}b + 4 = \frac{1}{8}b + 88$
224

11. $\frac{2}{5}w - w = -\frac{1}{5}(3w + 2)$
no solution

12. $5(p + 3) + 9 = 3(p - 2) + 6$
−12

13. $\frac{3}{4}k - 5 = \frac{1}{4}k - 1$
8

14. $0.03g - (2g + 3) = 1.8$
$-\dfrac{480}{197}$

15. $-5(2r + 3) = 3(11 - 4r) - 58$
−5

3-6

Study Guide

Solving Equations and Formulas

If an equation that contains more than one variable is to be solved for a specific variable, use the properties of equality to isolate the specified variable on one side of the equation.

Example: Solve $ax - b = c$ for x.

$$ax - b = c$$

$$ax - b + b = c + b \quad \text{Add } b \text{ to each side.}$$

$$ax = c + b$$

$$\frac{ax}{a} = \frac{c + b}{a} \quad \text{Divide each side by } a.$$

$$x = \frac{c + b}{a} \quad a \neq 0$$

Solve for x.

1. $15x + 1 = y$

2. $x + 45z = 90$

3. $(x + f) + 2 = j$

4. $xy + z = 9$

5. $x(4 - k) = p$

6. $7x + 3y = m$

7. $2x + b = c$

8. $x(1 + y) = z$

9. $16z + 4x = y$

10. Health The formula $H = \dfrac{34 - A}{2}$ is sometimes used to relate a person's age, A, to the number of hours of sleep they need every day, H.

a. Does this formula work for you? If not, why not?

b. For what ages does the formula seem to work best?

c. Solve the formula for A.

d. How old is a person who is getting his or her optimal amount of sleep, 8 hours per day?

Solving Equations and Formulas

If an equation that contains more than one variable is to be solved for a specific variable, use the properties of equality to isolate the specified variable on one side of the equation.

Example: Solve $ax - b = c$ for x.

$$ax - b = c$$

$$ax - b + b = c + b \quad \text{Add } b \text{ to each side.}$$

$$ax = c + b$$

$$\frac{ax}{a} = \frac{c + b}{a} \quad \text{Divide each side by } a.$$

$$x = \frac{c + b}{a} \quad a \neq 0$$

Solve for x.

1. $15x + 1 = y$

   $x = \dfrac{y - 1}{15}$

2. $x + 45z = 90$

   $x = 90 - 45z$

3. $(x + f) + 2 = j$

   $x = j - 2 - f$

4. $xy + z = 9$

   $x = \dfrac{9 - z}{y}, y \neq 0$

5. $x(4 - k) = p$

   $x = \dfrac{p}{4 - k}, k \neq 4$

6. $7x + 3y = m$

   $x = \dfrac{m - 3y}{7}$

7. $2x + b = c$

   $x = \dfrac{c - b}{2}$

8. $x(1 + y) = z$

   $x = \dfrac{z}{1 + y}, y \neq -1$

9. $16z + 4x = y$

   $x = \dfrac{y - 16z}{4}$

10. **Health** The formula $H = \dfrac{34 - A}{2}$ is sometimes used to relate a person's age, A, to the number of hours of sleep they need every day, H.

    a. Does this formula work for you? If not, why not? **probably**

    b. For what ages does the formula seem to work best? **0–20 years**

    c. Solve the formula for A. **$A = 34 - 2H$**

    d. How old is a person who is getting his or her optimal amount of sleep, 8 hours per day? **18**

NAME_____ DATE _____

Study Guide

Integration: Statistics
Measures of Central Tendency

In working with statistical data, it is often useful to have one value represent the complete set of data. For example, **measures of central tendency** represent centralized values of the data. Three measures of central tendency are the **mean, median,** and **mode.**

	Definitions	Examples
Mean	Sum of the elements in the set divided by the number of elements in the set.	**Data:** 24, 36, 21, 30, 21, 30 $$\frac{24 + 36 + 21 + 30 + 21 + 30}{6} = 27$$
Median	The middle of a set of data when the numbers are arranged in numerical order. In an even number of elements, the median is halfway between the two middle elements.	**Data:** 21, 21, 25, 30, 31, 42 $$\frac{25 + 30}{2} = 27.5$$
Mode	The number that occurs most often in a set of data.	**Data:** 21, 21, 24, 30, 30, 36 There are two modes, 21 and 30.

Find the mean, median, and mode for each set of data.

1.

Month	Days above 90°F
May	4
June	7
July	14
August	12
September	8

2.

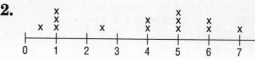

3. 3, 6, 6, 3, 6, 6, 3, 3

4. 19, 3, 0, 1

5. $\frac{1}{4}, \frac{2}{5}, \frac{2}{8}, \frac{1}{3}$

6. $1, \frac{1}{2}, 2, \frac{1}{3}, 3, \frac{1}{4}, 4, \frac{1}{8}$

Find the median and mode(s) of the data shown in each stem-and-leaf plot.

7.
Stem	Leaf
2	4 7 7
3	1 2 6 6 6 9
4	0
5	8 8 9

$3|2 = 32$

8.
Stem	Leaf
9	0 0 1 3 9
10	2 2 5
11	
12	0 3 3 8 8 9

$10|5 = 105$

Algebra 1

Study Guide

Integration: Statistics
Measures of Central Tendency

In working with statistical data, it is often useful to have one value represent the complete set of data. For example, **measures of central tendency** represent centralized values of the data. Three measures of central tendency are the **mean, median,** and **mode.**

	Definitions	Examples
Mean	Sum of the elements in the set divided by the number of elements in the set.	**Data:** 24, 36, 21, 30, 21, 30 $\dfrac{24 + 36 + 21 + 30 + 21 + 30}{6} = 27$
Median	The middle of a set of data when the numbers are arranged in numerical order. In an even number of elements, the median is halfway between the two middle elements.	**Data:** 21, 21, 25, 30, 31, 42 $\dfrac{25 + 30}{2} = 27.5$
Mode	The number that occurs most often in a set of data.	**Data:** 21, 21, 24, 30, 30, 36 There are two modes, 21 and 30.

Find the mean, median, and mode for each set of data.

1.

Month	Days above 90°F
May	4
June	7
July	14
August	12
September	8

9; 8; none

2.

3.7; 4; 1 and 5

3. 3, 6, 6, 3, 6, 6, 3, 3
   4.5, 4.5, 3 and 6

4. 19, 3, 0, 1
   5.75; 2; none

5. $\dfrac{1}{4}, \dfrac{2}{5}, \dfrac{2}{8}, \dfrac{1}{3}$
   $\dfrac{37}{120}; \dfrac{7}{24}; \dfrac{1}{4}$

6. $1, \dfrac{1}{2}, 2, \dfrac{1}{3}, 3, \dfrac{1}{4}, 4, \dfrac{1}{8}$
   $\dfrac{269}{192}; \dfrac{3}{4};$ **none**

Find the median and mode(s) of the data shown in each stem-and-leaf plot.

7.

Stem	Leaf
2	4 7 7
3	1 2 6 6 6 9
4	0
5	8 8 9

$3 | 2 = 32$
36; 36

8.

Stem	Leaf
9	0 0 1 3 9
10	2 2 5
11	
12	0 3 3 8 8 9

$10 | 5 = 105$
103.5; 90, 102, 123, 128

Algebra 1

Ratios and Proportions

In mathematics, a **ratio** compares two numbers by division. A ratio that compares a number a to a number b can be written in the following ways.

$$a \text{ to } b \qquad\qquad a{:}b \qquad\qquad \frac{a}{b}$$

When a ratio compares two quantities with different units of measure, that ratio is called a **rate.** For example, a 5°C rise in temperature per hour is a rate and can be expressed as $\dfrac{5 \text{ degrees}}{1 \text{ hour}}$, or 5 degrees per hour.

Proportions are often used to solve problems involving ratios. You can use the means-extremes property of proportions to solve equations that have the form of a proportion.

Definition of Proportion	An equation of the form $\frac{a}{b} = \frac{c}{d}$ stating that two ratios are equal is called a proportion.
Means-Extremes Property of Proportions	In a proportion, the product of the extremes is equal to the product of the means. If $\frac{a}{b} = \frac{c}{d}$, then $ad = bc$.

Example: Solve $\dfrac{x}{5} = \dfrac{10}{13}$.

$$\frac{x}{5} = \frac{10}{13}$$
$$13x = 50$$
$$x = 3\frac{11}{13}$$

The solution is $3\dfrac{11}{13}$.

Solve each proportion.

1. $\dfrac{0.1}{2} = \dfrac{0.5}{x}$

2. $\dfrac{x + 1}{4} = \dfrac{3}{4}$

3. $\dfrac{4}{6} = \dfrac{8}{x}$

4. $\dfrac{x}{21} = \dfrac{3}{63}$

5. $\dfrac{9}{y + 1} = \dfrac{18}{54}$

6. $\dfrac{3 - x}{4 + x} = \dfrac{8}{48}$

7. $\dfrac{4x}{25} = \dfrac{85 - x}{100}$

8. $\dfrac{x + 8}{-3} = \dfrac{17 - x}{-2}$

Use a proportion to solve each problem.

9. To make a model of the Guadelupe River bed, Hermie used 1 inch of clay for 5 miles of the actual river's length. His model river was 50 inches long. How long is the Guadelupe River?

10. Josh finished 24 math problems in one hour. At that rate, how many hours will it take him to complete 72 problems?

Study Guide

Ratios and Proportions

In mathematics, a **ratio** compares two numbers by division. A ratio that compares a number a to a number b can be written in the following ways.

$$a \text{ to } b \qquad\qquad a{:}b \qquad\qquad \frac{a}{b}$$

When a ratio compares two quantities with different units of measure, that ratio is called a **rate.** For example, a 5°C rise in temperature per hour is a rate and can be expressed as $\frac{5 \text{ degrees}}{1 \text{ hour}}$, or 5 degrees per hour.

Proportions are often used to solve problems involving ratios. You can use the means-extremes property of proportions to solve equations that have the form of a proportion.

Definition of Proportion	An equation of the form $\frac{a}{b} = \frac{c}{d}$ stating that two ratios are equal is called a proportion.
Means-Extremes Property of Proportions	In a proportion, the product of the extremes is equal to the product of the means. If $\frac{a}{b} = \frac{c}{d}$, then $ad = bc$.

Example: Solve $\frac{x}{5} = \frac{10}{13}$.

$$\frac{x}{5} = \frac{10}{13}$$
$$13x = 50$$
$$x = 3\frac{11}{13}$$

The solution is $3\frac{11}{13}$.

Solve each proportion.

1. $\dfrac{0.1}{2} = \dfrac{0.5}{x}$ **10**

2. $\dfrac{x+1}{4} = \dfrac{3}{4}$ **2**

3. $\dfrac{4}{6} = \dfrac{8}{x}$ **12**

4. $\dfrac{x}{21} = \dfrac{3}{63}$ **1**

5. $\dfrac{9}{y+1} = \dfrac{18}{54}$ **26**

6. $\dfrac{3-x}{4+x} = \dfrac{8}{48}$ **2**

7. $\dfrac{4x}{25} = \dfrac{85-x}{100}$ **5**

8. $\dfrac{x+8}{-3} = \dfrac{17-x}{-2}$ **7**

Use a proportion to solve each problem.

9. To make a model of the Guadelupe River bed, Hermie used 1 inch of clay for 5 miles of the actual river's length. His model river was 50 inches long. How long is the Guadelupe River? **250 miles**

10. Josh finished 24 math problems in one hour. At that rate, how many hours will it take him to complete 72 problems? **3 hours**

Algebra 1

4-2

Study Guide

Integration: Geometry
Similar Triangles

Triangle *RST* is *similar* to triangle *XYZ*. The angles of the two triangles are congruent. They are called **corresponding angles.** The sides opposite corresponding angles are called **corresponding sides.** Proportions can be used to find the missing measures of similar triangles.

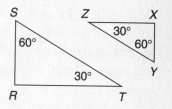

Similar Triangles	If two triangles are similar, the measures of their corresponding angles are equal and the measures of their corresponding sides are proportional.

Example: Find the height of the apartment building.

$\triangle ABC$ is similar to $\triangle AED$.

$$\frac{ED}{BC} = \frac{AD}{AC}$$

$$\frac{7}{x} = \frac{25}{300}$$

$$25x = 2100$$

$$x = 84$$

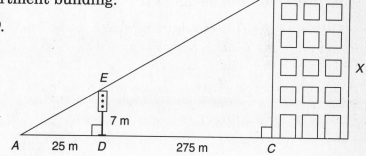

The apartment building is 84 meters high.

Refer to the triangles at the right to answer the questions.

1. Which triangles are similar?

2. Name corresponding angles of the similar triangles.

3. Name corresponding sides of the similar triangles.

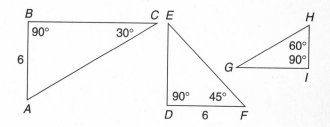

Solve.

4. Bruce likes to amuse his brother by shining a flashlight on his hand and making a shadow on the wall. How far is it from the flashlight to the wall?

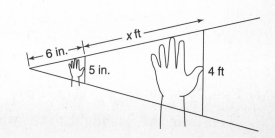

Integration: Geometry
Similar Triangles

Triangle *RST* is *similar* to triangle *XYZ*. The angles
of the two triangles are congruent. They are called
corresponding angles. The sides opposite
corresponding angles are called **corresponding
sides.** Proportions can be used to find the missing
measures of similar triangles.

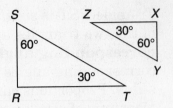

Similar Triangles	If two triangles are similar, the measures of their corresponding angles are equal and the measures of their corresponding sides are proportional.

Example: Find the height of the apartment building.

△*ABC* is similar to △*AED*.

$$\frac{ED}{BC} = \frac{AD}{AC}$$

$$\frac{7}{x} = \frac{25}{300}$$

$$25x = 2100$$

$$x = 84$$

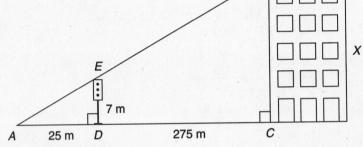

The apartment building is 84 meters high.

Refer to the triangles at the right to answer the questions.

1. Which triangles are similar?
   △ABC and △HIG

2. Name corresponding angles
   of the similar triangles.
   **∠A and ∠H; ∠B and ∠I;
   ∠C and ∠G**

3. Name corresponding sides of
   the similar triangles.
   AB and HI; AC and HG; BC and IG

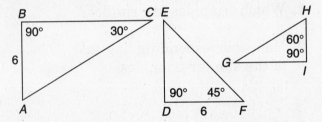

Solve.

4. Bruce likes to amuse his brother by
   shining a flashlight on his hand and
   making a shadow on the wall. How far
   is it from the flashlight to the wall?
   4.3 ft

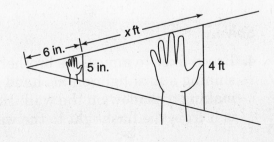

NAME_____ DATE _____

Study Guide

Integration: Trigonometry
Trigonometric Ratios

For each angle of every right triangle, certain ratios can be set up. These ratios are called **trigonometric ratios.** Study the triangle and then the chart below.

For angle A:
$\overline{BC}$ is *opposite* angle A.
$\overline{AC}$ is *adjacent* to angle A.
$\overline{AB}$ is the *hypotenuse* and is opposite the right angle C.

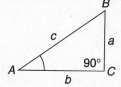

Definition of Trigonometric Ratios	
sine of angle $A = \dfrac{\text{measure of leg opposite angle } A}{\text{measure of hypotenuse}}$	$\sin A = \dfrac{a}{c}$
cosine of angle $A = \dfrac{\text{measure of leg adjacent angle } A}{\text{measure of hypotenuse}}$	$\cos A = \dfrac{b}{c}$
tangent of angle $A = \dfrac{\text{measure of leg opposite angle } A}{\text{measure of leg adjacent to angle } A}$	$\tan A = \dfrac{a}{b}$

Example 1: Find $\sin A$ to the nearest thousandth.

$$\sin A = \frac{a}{c} = \frac{5}{10} = 0.500$$

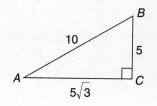

Example 2: Use a calculator to find the measure of angle A if $\sin A = 0.500$.

ENTER: 0.5 [INV] [SIN]   Result: 30

The measure of angle A is $30°$.

Find the sine, cosine, and tangent of each acute angle. Round your answers to the nearest thousandth.

1.

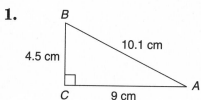

Use a calculator to find the value of each trigonometric ratio to the nearest ten thousandth.

2. $\sin 45°$ 3. $\cos 45°$ 4. $\tan 45°$ 5. $\sin 47°$ 6. $\cos 48°$

Use a calculator to find the measure of each angle to the nearest degree.

7. $\sin A = 0.7547$ 8. $\tan C = 1.1106$ 9. $\cos B = 0.6947$

Study Guide

Integration: Trigonometry
Trigonometric Ratios

For each angle of every right triangle, certain ratios can be set up. These ratios are called **trigonometric ratios.** Study the triangle and then the chart below.

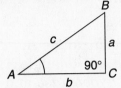

For angle A:
$\overline{BC}$ is *opposite* angle A.
$\overline{AC}$ is *adjacent* to angle A.
$\overline{AB}$ is the *hypotenuse* and is opposite the right angle C.

Definition of Trigonometric Ratios	
sine of angle $A = \dfrac{\text{measure of leg opposite angle } A}{\text{measure of hypotenuse}}$	$\sin A = \dfrac{a}{c}$
cosine of angle $A = \dfrac{\text{measure of leg adjacent angle } A}{\text{measure of hypotenuse}}$	$\cos A = \dfrac{b}{c}$
tangent of angle $A = \dfrac{\text{measure of leg opposite angle } A}{\text{measure of leg adjacent to angle } A}$	$\tan A = \dfrac{a}{b}$

Example 1: Find $\sin A$ to the nearest thousandth.

$$\sin A = \frac{a}{c} = \frac{5}{10} = 0.500$$

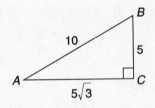

Example 2: Use a calculator to find the measure of angle A if $\sin A = 0.500$.

ENTER: 0.5 [INV] [SIN]   Result: 30

The measure of angle A is 30°.

Find the sine, cosine, and tangent of each acute angle. Round your answers to the nearest thousandth.

1.

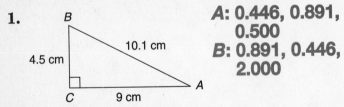

A: **0.446, 0.891, 0.500**
B: **0.891, 0.446, 2.000**

Use a calculator to find the value of each trigonometric ratio to the nearest ten thousandth.

2. $\sin 45°$ 3. $\cos 45°$ 4. $\tan 45°$ 5. $\sin 47°$ 6. $\cos 48°$
   0.7071   **0.7071**   **1.0000**   **0.7314**   **0.6691**

Use a calculator to find the measure of each angle to the nearest degree.

7. $\sin A = 0.7547$ 8. $\tan C = 1.1106$ 9. $\cos B = 0.6947$
   49°   **48°**   **46°**

NAME_____ DATE _____

Study Guide

Percents

A percent problem may be easier to solve if a proportion is used.

Percent Proportion
$\dfrac{\text{percentage}}{\text{base}} = \text{rate}$
or
$\dfrac{\text{percentage}}{\text{base}} = \dfrac{r}{100}$

Example 1: 25 is what percent of 30?

$$\begin{array}{c}\text{percentage} \rightarrow \\ \text{base} \rightarrow \end{array} \dfrac{25}{30} = \dfrac{r}{100} \leftarrow \text{rate}$$

$$2500 = 30r$$

$$83\frac{1}{3} = r$$

25 is $83\frac{1}{3}$% of 30.

Example 2: What number is 24% of 200?

$$\begin{array}{c}\text{percentage} \rightarrow \\ \text{base} \rightarrow \end{array} \dfrac{n}{200} = \dfrac{24}{100} \leftarrow \text{rate}$$

$$n = \dfrac{24}{100}(200)$$

$$= 48$$

48 is 24% of 200.

Use a proportion to answer each question.

1. Eight is what percent of 20?

2. Thirty is what percent of 50?

3. What is 75% of 24?

4. Find 60% of 90.

5. Twelve is 20% of what number?

6. 19.3 is 25% of what number?

7. On Wednesday Jean's Nursery received a shipment of 60 flowering crabapple trees. Jean had ordered 80 trees. What percent of her order arrived on Wednesday?

8. Phil received a commission of 5% on the sale of a house. If the amount of his commission was $4780, what was the selling price of the house?

Percents

A percent problem may be easier to solve if a proportion is used.

Percent Proportion
$\dfrac{\text{percentage}}{\text{base}} = \text{rate}$
or
$\dfrac{\text{percentage}}{\text{base}} = \dfrac{r}{100}$

Example 1: 25 is what percent of 30?

$$\text{percentage} \to \frac{25}{30} = \frac{r}{100} \leftarrow \text{rate}$$
$$\text{base} \to$$
$$2500 = 30r$$
$$83\frac{1}{3} = r$$

25 is $83\frac{1}{3}$% of 30.

Example 2: What number is 24% of 200?

$$\text{percentage} \to \frac{n}{200} = \frac{24}{100} \leftarrow \text{rate}$$
$$\text{base} \to$$
$$n = \frac{24}{100}(200)$$
$$= 48$$

48 is 24% of 200.

Use a proportion to answer each question.

1. Eight is what percent of 20?
40%

2. Thirty is what percent of 50?
60%

3. What is 75% of 24?
18

4. Find 60% of 90.
54

5. Twelve is 20% of what number?
60

6. 19.3 is 25% of what number?
77.2

7. On Wednesday Jean's Nursery received a shipment of 60 flowering crabapple trees. Jean had ordered 80 trees. What percent of her order arrived on Wednesday?
75%

8. Phil received a commission of 5% on the sale of a house. If the amount of his commission was $4780, what was the selling price of the house?
$95,600

Study Guide

Percent of Change

Some percent problems involve finding a percent of increase or decrease.

Percent of Increase	Percent of Decrease
A coat that cost $50 last year costs $55 this year. The price increased by $5 since last year.	Slacks that originally cost $30 are now on sale for $22. Find the percent of decrease.
$\dfrac{\text{amount of increase}\rightarrow}{\text{original price}\rightarrow}\ \dfrac{5}{50}=\dfrac{r}{100}$	$\dfrac{\text{amount of decrease}\rightarrow}{\text{original price}\rightarrow}\ \dfrac{8}{30}=\dfrac{r}{100}$
$500 = 50r$	$800 = 30r$
$10 = r$, or $r = 10$	$26\frac{2}{3} = r$, or $r = 26\frac{2}{3}$
The percent of increase is 10%.	The percent of decrease is $26\frac{2}{3}\%$, or about 27%.

The sales tax on a purchase is a percent of the purchase price. To find the total price, you must calculate the amount of sales tax and add it to the purchase price.

Find the final price of each item. When there is a discount and sales tax, compute the discount price first.

1. Compact Disc: $16.00
   Discount: 15%

2. Two concert tickets: $28.00
   Student discount: 28%

3. Airline Ticket: $248.00
   Superair discount: 33%

4. Celebrity Photo Calendar: $10.95
   Sales tax: 7.5%

5. Class Ring: $89.00
   Group discount: 17%
   Sales tax: 5%

6. Computer Software: $44.00
   Discount: 21%
   Sales tax: 6%

Solve each problem.

7. The original selling price of a new sports video was $65.00. Due to demand the price was increased to $87.75. What was the percent of increase over the original price?

8. A high school paper increased its sales by 75% when it ran an issue featuring a contest to win a class party. Before the contest issue, 10% of the school's 800 students bought the paper. How many students bought the contest issue?

Algebra 1

Study Guide

Percent of Change

Some percent problems involve finding a percent of increase or decrease.

Percent of Increase	Percent of Decrease
A coat that cost $50 last year costs $55 this year. The price increased by $5 since last year.	Slacks that originally cost $30 are now on sale for $22. Find the percent of decrease.
$\dfrac{\text{amount of increase}}{\text{original price}} \rightarrow \dfrac{5}{50} = \dfrac{r}{100}$	$\dfrac{\text{amount of decrease}}{\text{original price}} \rightarrow \dfrac{8}{30} = \dfrac{r}{100}$
$500 = 50r$	$800 = 30r$
$10 = r$, or $r = 10$	$26\frac{2}{3} = r$, or $r = 26\frac{2}{3}$
The percent of increase is 10%.	The percent of decrease is $26\frac{2}{3}$%, or about 27%.

The sales tax on a purchase is a percent of the purchase price. To find the total price, you must calculate the amount of sales tax and add it to the purchase price.

Find the final price of each item. When there is a discount and sales tax, compute the discount price first.

1. Compact Disc: $16.00
   Discount: 15%
   $13.60

2. Two concert tickets: $28.00
   Student discount: 28%
   $20.16

3. Airline Ticket: $248.00
   Superair discount: 33%
   $166.16

4. Celebrity Photo Calendar: $10.95
   Sales tax: 7.5%
   $11.77

5. Class Ring: $89.00
   Group discount: 17%
   Sales tax: 5%
   $77.56

6. Computer Software: $44.00
   Discount: 21%
   Sales tax: 6%
   $36.85

Solve each problem.

7. The original selling price of a new sports video was $65.00. Due to demand the price was increased to $87.75. What was the percent of increase over the original price?
   35%

8. A high school paper increased its sales by 75% when it ran an issue featuring a contest to win a class party. Before the contest issue, 10% of the school's 800 students bought the paper. How many students bought the contest issue? **140**

Study Guide

Integration: Probability
Probability and Odds

The **probability** of an event is a ratio that tells how likely it is that the event will take place.

Definition of Probability
$P(\text{event}) = \dfrac{\text{number of favorable outcomes}}{\text{number of possible outcomes}}$

Example 1: Mr. Babcock picks 5 of the 25 students in his algebra class at random for a special project. What is the probability of being picked?

$$P(\text{being picked}) = \frac{\text{number of students picked}}{\text{total number of students}}$$

The probability of being picked is $\frac{5}{25}$ or $\frac{1}{5}$.

The probability of any event has a value from 0 to 1. If the probability of an event is 0, it is impossible for the event to occur. An event that is certain to occur has a probability of 1. This can be expressed as $0 \leq P(\text{event}) \leq 1$.

The odds of an event occurring is the ratio of the number of ways an event can occur (successes) to the number of ways the event cannot occur (failures).

Definition of Odds
$\text{Odds} = \dfrac{\text{number of successes}}{\text{number of failures}}$

Example 2: Find the odds that a member of Mr. Babcock's class will be picked for the special project.

Number of successes: 5   Number of failures: 20
Odds of being picked = number of successes : number of failures
= 5:20, or 1:4

Solve each problem.

1. There were 2 colas, 1 ginger ale, 5 cherry sodas, and 4 root beers in the cooler. What is the probability of pulling out a cola?

2. It will rain 8 times in November and snow 3 times. The other days it will be sunny. What is the probability of sun? the odds of sun?

There is a bowl of money at the carnival. The bowl contains 50 quarters, 75 dimes, 100 nickels, and 125 pennies.

3. If one coin is chosen, what is the probability that a quarter will be chosen?

4. What would be the odds of choosing a quarter if all the dimes were removed first?

5. What are the odds that a dime will not be chosen?

6. What are the odds of choosing a penny?

Study Guide

Integration: Probability
Probability and Odds

The **probability** of an event is
a ratio that tells how likely it
is that the event will take place.

Definition of Probability
$P(\text{event}) = \dfrac{\text{number of favorable outcomes}}{\text{number of possible outcomes}}$

Example 1: Mr. Babcock picks 5 of the 25 students in his
algebra class at random for a special project. What
is the probability of being picked?

$$P(\text{being picked}) = \frac{\text{number of students picked}}{\text{total number of students}}$$

The probability of being picked is $\dfrac{5}{25}$ or $\dfrac{1}{5}$.

The probability of any event has a value from 0 to 1. If the
probability of an event is 0, it is impossible for the event to
occur. An event that is certain to occur has a probability of 1.
This can be expressed as $0 \le P(\text{event}) \le 1$.

The odds of an event occurring is the ratio of
the number of ways an event can occur
(successes) to the number of ways the event
cannot occur (failures).

Definition of Odds
$\text{Odds} = \dfrac{\text{number of successes}}{\text{number of failures}}$

Example 2: Find the odds that a member of Mr. Babcock's class
will be picked for the special project.

Number of successes: 5   Number of failures: 20
Odds of being picked = number of successes : number of failures
= 5:20, or 1:4

Solve each problem.

1. There were 2 colas, 1 ginger ale,
5 cherry sodas, and 4 root beers in
the cooler. What is the probability
of pulling out a cola? $\dfrac{1}{6}$

2. It will rain 8 times in November and
snow 3 times. The other days it will be
sunny. What is the probability of sun?
the odds of sun? $\dfrac{19}{30}$; **19:11**

**There is a bowl of money at the carnival. The bowl contains
50 quarters, 75 dimes, 100 nickels, and 125 pennies.**

3. If one coin is chosen, what is the
probability that a quarter will be
chosen? $\dfrac{1}{7}$

4. What would be the odds of choosing a
quarter if all the dimes were removed
first? **2:9**

5. What are the odds that a dime will
not be chosen? **11:3**

6. What are the odds of choosing a
penny? **5:9**

Study Guide

Weighted Averages

You can use charts to solve mixture problems.

Example 1: Alice Gleason invested a portion of $32,000 at 9% interest and the balance at 11% interest. How much did she invest at each rate if her total income from both investments was $3200.

Amount Invested	Rate	Annual Income
x	0.09	0.09x
32,000 − x	0.11	0.11(32,000 − x)

$$\underset{\text{9\% investment}}{\text{income from}} + \underset{\text{11\% investment}}{\text{income from}} = \underset{\text{income}}{\text{total}}$$

$$0.09x + 0.11(32,000 - x) = 3200$$
$$0.09x + 3520 - 0.11x = 3200$$
$$-0.02x = -320$$
$$x = 16,000$$
$$32,000 - x = 16,000$$

Ms. Gleason invested $16,000 at 9% and $16,000 at 11%.

When an object moves without changing its speed, it is said to be in **uniform motion.** The formula $d = rt$ is used to solve uniform motion problems.

Example 2: Bill Gutierrez left home driving at a speed of 54 miles per hour. How many hours did it take him to reach his destination 243 miles away?

$$d = rt$$
$$243 = 54t$$
$$4\frac{1}{2} = t$$

It will take Bill $4\frac{1}{2}$ hours to drive 243 miles.

Solve.

1. How many grams of sugar must be added to 60 grams of a 32% solution to obtain a 50% solution?

2. Mr. Anders and Ms. Rich each drove home from a business meeting. Mr. Anders traveled east at 100 kilometers per hour and Ms. Rich traveled west at 80 kilometers per hour. In how many hours were they 100 kilometers apart?

3. The Quick Mart has two kinds of nuts. Pecans sell for $1.55 per pound and walnuts sell for $1.95 per pound. How many pounds of walnuts must be added to 15 pounds of pecans to make a mixture that sells for $1.75 per pound?

4. Justin left home at 8:00 A.M., riding his bike at 6 miles per hour. His brother Joshua left 2 hours later, riding his bike at 8 miles per hour. At what time will Joshua catch up to Justin if Joshua is delayed 15 minutes by a freight train?

Weighted Averages

You can use charts to solve mixture problems.

Example 1: Alice Gleason invested a portion of $32,000 at 9% interest and the balance at 11% interest. How much did she invest at each rate if her total income from both investments was $3200.

Amount Invested	Rate	Annual Income
x	0.09	$0.09x$
$32,000 - x$	0.11	$0.11(32,000 - x)$

$$\underset{\text{9\% investment}}{\text{income from}} + \underset{\text{11\% investment}}{\text{income from}} = \underset{\text{income}}{\text{total}}$$

$$0.09x + 0.11(32,000 - x) = 3200$$
$$0.09x + 3520 - 0.11x = 3200$$
$$-0.02x = -320$$
$$x = 16,000$$
$$32,000 - x = 16,000$$

Ms. Gleason invested $16,000 at 9% and $16,000 at 11%.

When an object moves without changing its speed, it is said to be in **uniform motion.** The formula $d = rt$ is used to solve uniform motion problems.

Example 2: Bill Gutierrez left home driving at a speed of 54 miles per hour. How many hours did it take him to reach his destination 243 miles away?

$$d = rt$$
$$243 = 54t$$
$$4\frac{1}{2} = t$$

It will take Bill $4\frac{1}{2}$ hours to drive 243 miles.

Solve.

1. How many grams of sugar must be added to 60 grams of a 32% solution to obtain a 50% solution?
21.6 grams

2. Mr. Anders and Ms. Rich each drove home from a business meeting. Mr. Anders traveled east at 100 kilometers per hour and Ms. Rich traveled west at 80 kilometers per hour. In how many hours were they 100 kilometers apart?
$\frac{5}{9}$ **hour**

3. The Quick Mart has two kinds of nuts. Pecans sell for $1.55 per pound and walnuts sell for $1.95 per pound. How many pounds of walnuts must be added to 15 pounds of pecans to make a mixture that sells for $1.75 per pound? **15 pounds**

4. Justin left home at 8:00 A.M., riding his bike at 6 miles per hour. His brother Joshua left 2 hours later, riding his bike at 8 miles per hour. At what time will Joshua catch up to Justin if Joshua is delayed 15 minutes by a freight train? **5 P.M.**

Study Guide

Direct and Inverse Variation

If two variables x and y are related by the equation $y = kx$, where k is a nonzero constant, then the equation is called a **direct variation,** and k is called the **constant of variation.** If two variables x and y are related by the equation $xy = k$, where $k \neq 0$, then the equation is called an **inverse variation.**

Example 1: If y varies directly as x, and $y = 12$ when $x = 4$, find y when $x = 7$.

$$y = kx \qquad\qquad y = kx$$
$$12 = 4k \qquad\qquad y = 3(7)$$
$$\frac{12}{4} = \frac{4k}{4} \qquad\qquad y = 21$$
$$3 = k$$

Example 2: If y varies inversely as x, and $y = 3$ when $x = 12$, find x when $y = 4$.

$$xy = k \qquad\qquad xy = k$$
$$12(3) = k \qquad\qquad 4x = 36$$
$$36 = k \qquad\qquad \frac{4x}{4} = \frac{36}{4}$$
$$\qquad\qquad\qquad x = 9$$

Solve. Assume that y varies directly as x.

1. If $y = 4$ when $x = 2$, find y when $x = 16$.

2. If $y = 9$ when $x = -3$, find x when $y = 6$.

3. If $y = \frac{2}{5}$ when $x = \frac{1}{3}$, find y when $x = \frac{1}{4}$.

4. If $y = \frac{1}{4}$ when $x = \frac{1}{8}$, find x when $y = \frac{3}{16}$.

Solve. Assume that y varies inversely as x.

5. If $y = 9$ when $x = 7$, find y when $x = 2$.

6. If $y = 4.3$ when $x = 12.9$, find y when $x = 15.8$.

7. If $x = \frac{1}{2}$ when $y = \frac{1}{3}$, find y when $x = \frac{1}{4}$.

8. If $y = -6$ when $x = \frac{1}{4}$, find y when $x = \frac{3}{16}$.

Algebra 1

NAME_____ DATE _____

Study Guide

Direct and Inverse Variation

If two variables x and y are related by the equation $y = kx$, where k is a nonzero constant, then the equation is called a **direct variation,** and k is called the **constant of variation.** If two variables x and y are related by the equation $xy = k$, where $k \neq 0$, then the equation is called an **inverse variation.**

Example 1: If y varies directly as x, and $y = 12$ when $x = 4$, find y when $x = 7$.

$$
\begin{array}{l|l}
y = kx & y = kx \\
12 = 4k & y = 3(7) \\
\dfrac{12}{4} = \dfrac{4k}{4} & y = 21 \\
3 = k &
\end{array}
$$

Example 2: If y varies inversely as x, and $y = 3$ when $x = 12$, find x when $y = 4$.

$$
\begin{array}{l|l}
xy = k & xy = k \\
12(3) = k & 4x = 36 \\
36 = k & \dfrac{4x}{4} = \dfrac{36}{4} \\
& x = 9
\end{array}
$$

Solve. Assume that y varies directly as x.

1. If $y = 4$ when $x = 2$, find y when $x = 16$.

32

2. If $y = 9$ when $x = -3$, find x when $y = 6$.

−2

3. If $y = \dfrac{2}{5}$ when $x = \dfrac{1}{3}$, find y when $x = \dfrac{1}{4}$.

$\dfrac{3}{10}$

4. If $y = \dfrac{1}{4}$ when $x = \dfrac{1}{8}$, find x when $y = \dfrac{3}{16}$.

$\dfrac{3}{32}$

Solve. Assume that y varies inversely as x.

5. If $y = 9$ when $x = 7$, find y when $x = 2$.

$\dfrac{63}{2}$

6. If $y = 4.3$ when $x = 12.9$, find y when $x = 15.8$.

$\dfrac{5547}{1580}$

7. If $x = \dfrac{1}{2}$ when $y = \dfrac{1}{3}$, find y when $x = \dfrac{1}{4}$.

$\dfrac{2}{3}$

8. If $y = -6$ when $x = \dfrac{1}{4}$, find y when $x = \dfrac{3}{16}$.

−8

Algebra 1

Study Guide

The Coordinate Plane

In the diagram at the right, the two perpendicular lines, called the *x*-axis and the *y*-axis, divide the coordinate plane into Quadrants I, II, III, and IV. The point where the two axes intersect is called the origin. The origin is represented by the ordered pair (0, 0).

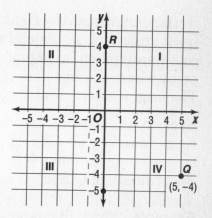

Every other point in the coordinate plane is also represented by an ordered pair of numbers. The ordered pair for point *Q* is (5, −4). We say that 5 is the *x*-coordinate of *Q* and −4 is the *y*-coordinate of *Q*.

Example: Write the ordered pair for the point *R* above.

The *x*-coordinate is 0 and the *y*-coordinate is 4. Thus, the ordered pair for *R* is (0, 4).

To graph any ordered pair (*x*, *y*), begin at the origin. Move left or right *x* units. From there, move up or down *y* units. Draw a dot at that point.

Graph each point on the coordinate plane at the right.

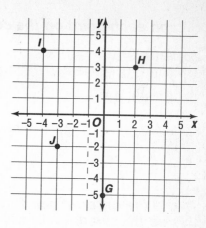

1. *A* (0, 0)

2. *B* (5, 0)

3. *C* (−3, 4)

4. *D* (4, −5)

5. *E* (−2, −3)

6. *F* (2, −1)

**Write the ordered pair for each point shown at the right.
Name the quadrant in which the point is located.**

7. *G*   8. *H*   9. *I*   10. *J*

5-1

Study Guide

Student Edition
Pages 254–259

The Coordinate Plane

In the diagram at the right, the two perpendicular lines, called the *x*-axis and the *y*-axis, divide the coordinate plane into Quadrants I, II, III, and IV. The point where the two axes intersect is called the origin. The origin is represented by the ordered pair (0, 0).

Every other point in the coordinate plane is also represented by an ordered pair of numbers. The ordered pair for point *Q* is (5, −4). We say that 5 is the *x*-coordinate of *Q* and −4 is the *y*-coordinate of *Q*.

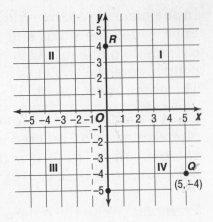

Example: Write the ordered pair for the point *R* above.

　　　The *x*-coordinate is 0 and the *y*-coordinate is 4. Thus, the ordered pair for *R* is (0, 4).

To graph any ordered pair (*x*, *y*), begin at the origin. Move left or right *x* units. From there, move up or down *y* units. Draw a dot at that point.

Graph each point on the coordinate plane at the right.

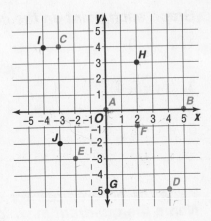

1. *A* (0, 0)

2. *B* (5, 0)

3. *C* (−3, 4)

4. *D* (4, −5)

5. *E* (−2, −3)

6. *F* (2, −1)

Write the ordered pair for each point shown at the right. Name the quadrant in which the point is located.

7. *G*
(0, −5);
none

8. *H*
(2, 3);
I

9. *I*
(−4, 4);
II

10. *J*
(−3, −2);
III

5-2

Study Guide

Relations

A **relation** is a set of ordered pairs. The **domain** of a relation is the set of all first coordinates of the ordered pairs, and the **range** is the set of all second coordinates.

Example 1: State the domain and range of each relation.
1. {(3, 3), (3, 4), (3, 5)} Domain = {3}; Range = {3, 4, 5}
2. {(1, 2), (2, 1), (3, 2)} Domain = {1, 2, 3}; Range = {1, 2}

Relations may be expressed in the form of ordered pairs, tables, graphs, and mappings.

Example 2: The relation {(1, 1), (0, 2), (3, −2)} can be expressed in each of the following ways.

Ordered pairs
(1, 1)
(0, 2)
(3, −2)

Table

x	y
1	1
0	2
3	−2

Graph

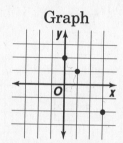

Mapping

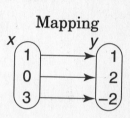

The **inverse** of any relation is obtained by switching the coordinates in each ordered pair.

State the domain and range of each relation.

1. {(−6, 5), (−3, 8), (−6, 9), (3, 11)}

2. {(0.8, −0.8), (1.2, 0), (3.5, 4)}

3. $\left\{\left(\frac{1}{2}, \frac{1}{4}\right), \left(1\frac{1}{2}, 1\frac{1}{4}\right), \left(3\frac{1}{2}, 2\right)\right\}$

Express the relations shown in each table, mapping, or graph as a set of ordered pairs. Then state the domain, range, and inverse of the relation.

4.

x	y
1	3
2	4
3	6

5.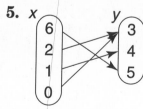

Draw a mapping and graph for each relation.

6. {(−2, −1), (3, 3), (4, 3)}

7. {(0, 0), (1, 1), (2, 2)}

Study Guide

Relations

A **relation** is a set of ordered pairs. The **domain** of a relation is the set of all first coordinates of the ordered pairs, and the **range** is the set of all second coordinates.

Example 1: State the domain and range of each relation.
   1. {(3, 3), (3, 4), (3, 5)} Domain = {3}; Range = {3, 4, 5}
   2. {(1, 2), (2, 1), (3, 2)} Domain = {1, 2, 3}; Range = {1, 2}

Relations may be expressed in the form of ordered pairs, tables, graphs, and mappings.

Example 2: The relation {(1, 1), (0, 2), (3, −2)} can be expressed in each of the following ways.

Ordered pairs	Table	Graph	Mapping
(1, 1) (0, 2) (3, −2)			

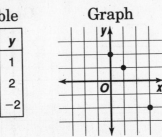

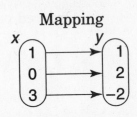

x	y
1	1
0	2
3	−2

The **inverse** of any relation is obtained by switching the coordinates in each ordered pair.

State the domain and range of each relation.

1. {(−6, 5), (−3, 8), (−6, 9), (3, 11)} D = {−6, −3, 3}; R = {5, 8, 9, 11}

2. {(0.8, −0.8), (1.2, 0), (3.5, 4)} D = {0.8, 1.2, 3.5}; R = {−0.8, 0, 4}

3. $\left\{\left(\frac{1}{2}, \frac{1}{4}\right), \left(1\frac{1}{2}, 1\frac{1}{4}\right), \left(3\frac{1}{2}, 2\right)\right\}$ D = $\left\{\frac{1}{2}, 1\frac{1}{2}, 3\frac{1}{2}\right\}$; R = $\left\{\frac{1}{4}, 1\frac{1}{4}, 2\right\}$

Express the relations shown in each table, mapping, or graph as a set of ordered pairs. Then state the domain, range, and inverse of the relation.

4.
x	y
1	3
2	4
3	6

{(1, 3), (2, 4), (3, 6)}
D = {1, 2, 3}
R = {3, 4, 6}
I = {(3, 1), (4, 2), (6, 3)}

5.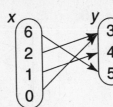

{(6, 5), (2, 3), (1, 4), (0, 3)}
D = {0, 1, 2, 6}
R = {3, 4, 5}
I = {(5, 6), (3, 2), (4, 1), (3, 0)}

Draw a mapping and graph for each relation.

6. {(−2, −1), (3, 3), (4, 3)}

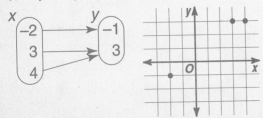

7. {(0, 0), (1, 1), (2, 2)}

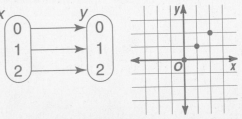

Algebra 1

NAME_____ DATE_____

Study Guide

Equations as Relations

An equation in two variables describes a relation. It is often easier to determine the solution of such an equation by solving for one of the variables.

Example: Solve $3y + 2x = 10$ if the domain is $\{-7, -1, 8\}$.

First solve for y in terms of x.

$$3y + 2x = 10$$
$$3y = 10 - 2x$$
$$y = \frac{10 - 2x}{3}$$

Then substitute values of x.

x	$\dfrac{10 - 2x}{3}$	y	(x, y)
-7	$\dfrac{10 - 2(-7)}{3}$	8	$(-7, 8)$
-1	$\dfrac{10 - 2(-1)}{3}$	4	$(-1, 4)$
8	$\dfrac{10 - 2(8)}{3}$	-2	$(8, -2)$

Which ordered pairs are solutions of each equation?

1. $y = 3x + 1$ **a.** $(0, 1)$ **b.** $\left(\frac{1}{3}, 2\right)$ **c.** $\left(-1, -\frac{2}{3}\right)$ **d.** $(-1, -2)$

2. $2a = 5 - b$ **a.** $(5, 0)$ **b.** $(5, -5)$ **c.** $\left(\frac{5}{2}, 0\right)$ **d.** $(1, -3)$

Solve each equation if the domain is $\{-4, -2, 0, 2, 4\}$.

3. $x + y = 4$ 4. $y = -4x - 6$ 5. $5a - 3b = 15$

6. $3x - 5y = 8$ 7. $6x + 3y = 18$ 8. $4x + 8 = 6y$

Study Guide

Equations as Relations

An equation in two variables describes a relation. It is often easier to determine the solution of such an equation by solving for one of the variables.

Example: Solve $3y + 2x = 10$ if the domain is $\{-7, -1, 8\}$.
First solve for y in terms of x.

$$3y + 2x = 10$$
$$3y = 10 - 2x$$
$$y = \frac{10 - 2x}{3}$$

Then substitute values of x.

x	$\dfrac{10 - 2x}{3}$	y	(x, y)
-7	$\dfrac{10 - 2(-7)}{3}$	8	$(-7, 8)$
-1	$\dfrac{10 - 2(-1)}{3}$	4	$(-1, 4)$
8	$\dfrac{10 - 2(8)}{3}$	-2	$(8, -2)$

Which ordered pairs are solutions of each equation?

1. $y = 3x + 1$ **a.** $(0, 1)$ **b.** $\left(\frac{1}{3}, 2\right)$ **c.** $\left(-1, -\frac{2}{3}\right)$ **d.** $(-1, -2)$
    a, b, d

2. $2a = 5 - b$ **a.** $(5, 0)$ **b.** $(5, -5)$ **c.** $\left(\frac{5}{2}, 0\right)$ **d.** $(1, -3)$
    b, c

Solve each equation if the domain is $\{-4, -2, 0, 2, 4\}$.

3. $x + y = 4$
$\{(-4, 8), (-2, 6),$
$(0, 4), (2, 2), (4, 0)\}$

4. $y = -4x - 6$
$\{(-4, 10), (-2, 2),$
$(0, -6), (2, -14),$
$(4, -22)\}$

5. $5a - 3b = 15$
$\left\{\left(-4, -11\frac{2}{3}\right), \left(-2, -8\frac{1}{3}\right),\right.$
$\left. (0, -5), \left(2, -1\frac{2}{3}\right), \left(4, 1\frac{2}{3}\right)\right\}$

6. $3x - 5y = 8$
$\left\{(-4, -4), \left(-2, -\frac{14}{5}\right),\right.$
$\left. \left(0, -\frac{8}{5}\right), \left(2, -\frac{2}{5}\right), \left(4, \frac{4}{5}\right)\right\}$

7. $6x + 3y = 18$
$\{(-4, 14), (-2, 10),$
$(0, 6), (2, 2), (4, -2)\}$

8. $4x + 8 = 6y$
$\left\{\left(-4, -\frac{4}{3}\right), (-2, 0),\right.$
$\left. \left(0, \frac{4}{3}\right), \left(2, \frac{8}{3}\right), (4, 4)\right\}$

Algebra 1

5-4

Study Guide

Graphing Linear Equations

An equation whose graph is a straight line is called a **linear equation**.

Definition of Linear Equation

A **linear equation** is an equation that can be written in the form $Ax + By = C$, where A, B, and C are any numbers and A and B are not both 0.

Drawing the Graph of a Linear Equation

1. Solve the equation for one variable.
2. Set up a table of values for the variables.
3. Graph the ordered pairs and connect them with a line.

Example: Draw the graph of $y - 3x = 1$.

$$y - 3x = 1$$
$$y = 3x + 1$$

x	3x + 1	y	(x, y)
−1	3(−1) + 1	−2	(−1, −2)
0	3(0) + 1	1	(0, 1)
1	3(1) + 1	4	(1, 4)

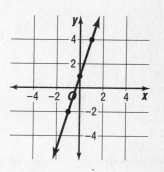

Determine whether each equation is a linear equation. If an equation is linear, rewrite it in the form $Ax + By = C$.

1. $4x - 2y = -1$

2. $\dfrac{x}{3} = 5$

3. $y = x^2 + 7$

Graph each equation.

4. $3x + 2y = 6$

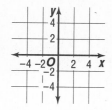

5. $m + 2n = 4$

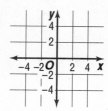

6. $3p + q = -2$

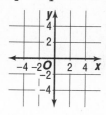

7. $3a - 6b = -3$

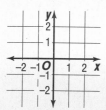

8. $-2x + y = -2$

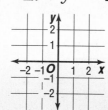

9. $\dfrac{1}{4}x + \dfrac{3}{4}y = 6$

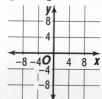

Algebra 1

NAME_____ DATE _____

Study Guide

Graphing Linear Equations

An equation whose graph is a straight line is called a **linear equation**.

Definition of Linear Equation
A **linear equation** is an equation that can be written in the form $Ax + By = C$, where A, B, and C are any numbers and A and B are not both 0.

Drawing the Graph of a Linear Equation

1. Solve the equation for one variable.
2. Set up a table of values for the variables.
3. Graph the ordered pairs and connect them with a line.

Example: Draw the graph of $y - 3x = 1$.

$$y - 3x = 1$$
$$y = 3x + 1$$

x	3x + 1	y	(x, y)
−1	3(−1) + 1	−2	(−1, −2)
0	3(0) + 1	1	(0, 1)
1	3(1) + 1	4	(1, 4)

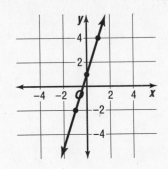

Determine whether each equation is a linear equation. If an equation is linear, rewrite it in the form Ax + By = C.

1. $4x - 2y = -1$ **yes;**
   $4x - 2y = -1$

2. $\frac{x}{3} = 5$ **yes;**
   $x = 15$

3. $y = x^2 + 7$ **no**

Graph each equation.

4. $3x + 2y = 6$

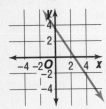

5. $m + 2n = 4$

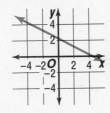

6. $3p + q = -2$

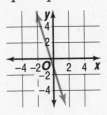

7. $3a - 6b = -3$

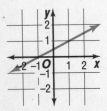

8. $-2x + y = -2$

9. $\frac{1}{4}x + \frac{3}{4}y = 6$

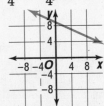

Algebra 1

Study Guide

Functions

A special type of relation is called a **function.**

Definition of Function
A **function** is a relation in which each element of the domain is paired with *exactly* one element of the range.

Example 1: Is $\{(6, -3), (4, 1), (7, -2), (-3, 1)\}$ a function? Is the inverse a function?

Since each element of the domain is paired with exactly one element of the range, the relation *is* a function. The inverse is not a function because 1 is paired with more than one element of the range.

The equation $y = 2x + 1$ can be written as $f(x) = 2x + 1$. If $x = 3$, then $f(3) = 2(3) + 1$, or 7. Thus, $f(3)$, which is read "f of 3" is a way of referring to the value of y that corresponds to $x = 3$.

Example: If $f(x) = 3x - 4$, find $f(3)$ and $f(-2)$.

$$f(3) = 3(3) - 4 \qquad f(-2) = 3(-2) - 4$$
$$= 9 - 4 \qquad\qquad\quad = -6 - 4$$
$$= 5 \qquad\qquad\qquad = -10$$

Determine whether each relation is a function.

1.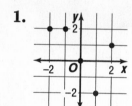

2.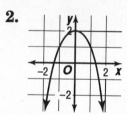

3.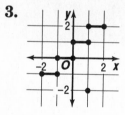

4. $\{(4, 2), (2, 3), (6, 1)\}$

5. $\{(-3, -3), (-3, 4), (-2, 4)\}$

6. $\{(-1, 0), (1, 0)\}$

7. $-2x + 4y = 0$

8. $x^2 + y^2 = 8$

9. $-\frac{1}{4}x = -\frac{1}{4}y - 2$

Given f(x) = 2x − 4 and g(x) = x² − 4x, find each value.

10. $f(4)$

11. $g(2)$

12. $f(-5)$

13. $g(-3)$

14. $f\left(\frac{1}{4}\right)$

15. $g\left(\frac{1}{4}\right)$

Algebra 1

Study Guide

Functions

A special type of relation is called a **function.**

Definition of Function
A **function** is a relation in which each element of the domain is paired with *exactly* one element of the range.

Example 1: Is {(6, −3), (4, 1), (7, −2), (−3, 1)} a function? Is the inverse a function?

Since each element of the domain is paired with exactly one element of the range, the relation *is* a function. The inverse is not a function because 1 is paired with more than one element of the range.

The equation $y = 2x + 1$ can be written as $f(x) = 2x + 1$. If $x = 3$, then $f(3) = 2(3) + 1$, or 7. Thus, $f(3)$, which is read "f of 3" is a way of referring to the value of y that corresponds to $x = 3$.

Example: If $f(x) = 3x − 4$, find $f(3)$ and $f(−2)$.

$$f(3) = 3(3) − 4 \qquad f(−2) = 3(−2) − 4$$
$$= 9 − 4 \qquad\qquad = −6 − 4$$
$$= 5 \qquad\qquad\quad = −10$$

Determine whether each relation is a function.

1. 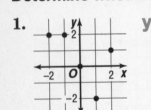 yes

2. 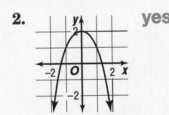 yes

3. 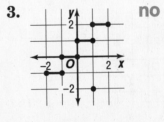 no

4. {(4, 2), (2, 3), (6, 1)}
   yes

5. {(−3, −3), (−3, 4), (−2, 4)}
   no

6. {(−1, 0), (1, 0)}
   yes

7. $−2x + 4y = 0$ yes

8. $x^2 + y^2 = 8$ no

9. $−\frac{1}{4}x = −\frac{1}{4}y − 2$ yes

Given $f(x) = 2x − 4$ and $g(x) = x^2 − 4x$, find each value.

10. $f(4)$
    4

11. $g(2)$
    −4

12. $f(−5)$
    −14

13. $g(−3)$
    21

14. $f\left(\frac{1}{4}\right)$
    $−3\frac{1}{2}$

15. $g\left(\frac{1}{4}\right)$
    $−\frac{15}{16}$

Study Guide

Writing Equations From Patterns

You can find equations from relations. Suppose you purchased a number of packages of blank cassette tapes. If each package contained three tapes, you could make a chart to show the relationship between the number of packages of blank cassette tapes and the number of tapes purchased. Use x for the number of packages and y for the number of tapes.

x	1	2	3	4	5	6
y	3	6	9	12	15	18

This relationship can also be shown as an equation. Since y is always three times x, the equation is $y = 3x$. Another way to discover this relationship is to study the difference between successive values of x and y.

+1 ⌒ +1 ⌒ +1 ⌒ +1 ⌒ +1 ⌒ +1

x	1	2	3	4	5	6
y	3	6	9	12	15	18

+3 ⌣ +3 ⌣ +3 ⌣ +3 ⌣ +3 ⌣ +3

This suggests the relation $y = 3x$.

Write an equation for each relation. Then complete each chart.

1.

x	−1	0	1	2	3	4
y	−2	2	6			

2.

x	−2	−1	0	1	2	3
y	10	7	4			

3.

x	−4	−3	−2	−1	0	1
y	$\frac{5}{2}$	$\frac{9}{4}$	2			

4.

x	0	1	2	3	4	5
y	3	$\frac{12}{5}$	$\frac{9}{5}$			

5. $\left\{ (-10, -5), (-4, -2), (0, 0), (2, 1), \left(5, \frac{5}{2}\right) \right\}$

6. $\{(-3, -10), (-1, -4), (0, -1), (2, 5), (4, 11)\}$

Writing Equations From Patterns

You can find equations from relations. Suppose you purchased a number of packages of blank cassette tapes. If each package contained three tapes, you could make a chart to show the relationship between the number of packages of blank cassette tapes and the number of tapes purchased. Use x for the number of packages and y for the number of tapes.

x	1	2	3	4	5	6
y	3	6	9	12	15	18

This relationship can also be shown as an equation. Since y is always three times x, the equation is $y = 3x$. Another way to discover this relationship is to study the difference between successive values of x and y.

+1 ⌒ +1 ⌒ +1 ⌒ +1 ⌒ +1 ⌒ +1

x	1	2	3	4	5	6
y	3	6	9	12	15	18

+3 ⌣ +3 ⌣ +3 ⌣ +3 ⌣ +3 ⌣ +3

This suggests the relation $y = 3x$.

Write an equation for each relation. Then complete each chart.

1.

x	−1	0	1	2	3	4
y	−2	2	6	10	14	18

$y = 4x + 2$

2.

x	−2	−1	0	1	2	3
y	10	7	4	1	−2	−5

$y = -3x + 4$

3.

x	−4	−3	−2	−1	0	1
y	$\frac{5}{2}$	$\frac{9}{4}$	2	$\frac{7}{4}$	$\frac{3}{2}$	$\frac{5}{4}$

$y = -\frac{1}{4}x + 1\frac{1}{2}$

4.

x	0	1	2	3	4	5
y	3	$\frac{12}{5}$	$\frac{9}{5}$	$\frac{6}{5}$	$\frac{3}{5}$	0

$y = -\frac{3}{5}x + 3$

5. $\left\{(-10, -5), (-4, -2), (0, 0), (2, 1), \left(5, \frac{5}{2}\right)\right\}$ $y = \frac{1}{2}x$

6. $\{(-3, -10), (-1, -4), (0, -1), (2, 5), (4, 11)\}$ $y = 3x - 1$

Algebra 1

5-7

Study Guide

Integration: Statistics
Measures of Variation

A *measure of variation* called the **range** describes the spread of numbers in a set of data. To find the range, determine the difference between the greatest and least value in the set.

Quartiles divide the data into four equal parts. The **upper quartile** divides the top half into two equal parts. The **lower quartile** divides the bottom half into two equal parts. Another measure of variation uses the upper and lower quartile values to determine the **interquartile range.** Study the data below.

		lower quartile┐				median = 66			upper quartile		
23	23	31	31	63	63	69	71	72	82	80	160

The lower quartile is the median of the lower half (31). The upper quartile is the median of the upper half (77). The range is 160 − 23 = 137. The interquartile range is 77 − 31 = 46.

Find the range, median, upper quartile, lower quartile, and interquartile range for each set of data.

1.

Month	Days below 32°F
November	5
December	20
January	21
February	15
March	8

2.

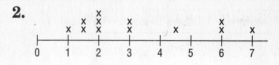

3. 4, 5, 5, 4, 4, 6, 5, 5, 5

4. 1, 7, 12, 10

5. 3, 0, 4, 9, 6, 4, 0, 1

6. 1.5, 0.5, 2, 3, 2.5

7.

Stem	Leaf
1	2 3 4 6 7 8
2	1 5 5 6 7 8 9
3	0 0 2 3

$2|5 = 250$

8.

Stem	Leaf
18	3 4 6 7
19	0 0 4
20	1 2 2 3 8 8
21	3 4 7

$20|3 = 20.3$

Solve.

9. In five pre-race trials a stock car driver recorded the following speeds in miles per hour: 155, 158, 163, 187, 172. Find the range and interquartile range.

10. The swimming times in seconds for the 50-yard butterfly were 36.30, 35.00, 31.60, 34.00, 35.52, 36.39, 38.87, and 41.62. Find the range, median, upper and lower quartiles, and interquartile range.

NAME _____ DATE _____

Study Guide

Student Edition
Pages 305–313

Integration: Statistics
Measures of Variation

A *measure of variation* called the **range** describes the spread of numbers in a set of data. To find the range, determine the difference between the greatest and least value in the set.

Quartiles divide the data into four equal parts. The **upper quartile** divides the top half into two equal parts. The **lower quartile** divides the bottom half into two equal parts. Another measure of variation uses the upper and lower quartile values to determine the **interquartile range.** Study the data below.

lower quartile →			↓			median = 66 ↓			upper quartile ↓		
23	23	31	31	63	63	69	71	72	82	80	160

The lower quartile is the median of the lower half (31). The upper quartile is the median of the upper half (77). The range is 160 − 23 = 137. The interquartile range is 77 − 31 = 46.

Find the range, median, upper quartile, lower quartile, and interquartile range for each set of data.

1.

Month	Days below 32°F
November	5
December	20
January	21
February	15
March	8

16; 15; 20.5; 6.5; 14

2.

6; 2.5; 5.25; 1.75; 3.5

3. 4, 5, 5, 4, 4, 6, 5, 5, 5
2; 5; 5; 4; 1

4. 1, 7, 12, 10
11; 8.5; 11; 4; 7

5. 3, 0, 4, 9, 6, 4, 0, 1
9; 3.5; 5; 0.5; 4.5

6. 1.5, 0.5, 2, 3, 2.5
2.5; 2; 2.75; 1; 1.75

7.

Stem	Leaf
1	2 3 4 6 7 8
2	1 5 5 6 7 8 9
3	0 0 2 3

2|5 = 250

210; 250; 295; 165; 130

Solve.

8.

Stem	Leaf
18	3 4 6 7
19	0 0 4
20	1 2 2 3 8 8
21	3 4 7

20|3 = 20.3

3.4; 20.15; 20.8; 18.85; 1.95

9. In five pre-race trials a stock car driver recorded the following speeds in miles per hour: 155, 158, 163, 187, 172. Find the range and interquartile range. **32; 23**

10. The swimming times in seconds for the 50-yard butterfly were 36.30, 35.00, 31.60, 34.00, 35.52, 36.39, 38.87, and 41.62. Find the range, median, upper and lower quartiles, and interquartile range. **10.02; 35.91; 37.63; 34.5; 3.13**

Algebra 1

Study Guide

Slope

The ratio of *rise* to *run* is called **slope**. The slope of a line describes its steepness, or rate of change.

On a coordinate plane, a line extending from lower left to upper right has a positive slope. A line extending from upper left to lower right has a negative slope. The slope of a horizontal line is zero. A vertical line has *no slope*.

The slope of a nonvertical line can be determined from the coordinates of any two points on the line.

Definition of Slope
The slope *m* of a line is the ratio of the change in the *y*-coordinates to the corresponding change in the *x*-coordinates.   Slope $= \dfrac{\text{change in } y}{\text{change in } x}$ or $m = \dfrac{\text{change in } y}{\text{change in } x}$

Determining Slope Given Two Points
Given the coordinates of two points, (x_1, y_1) and (x_2, y_2), on a line, the slope *m* can be found as follows: $m = \dfrac{y_2 - y_1}{x_2 - x_1}$, where $x_1 \neq x_2$.

Example: Determine the slope of the line that passes through $(-1, 5)$ and $(4, -2)$.

$$m = \frac{y_2 - y_1}{x_2 - x_1}$$

$$= \frac{-2 - 5}{4 - (-1)}$$

$$= \frac{-7}{5} = -\frac{7}{5}$$

Determine the slope of the line that passes through each pair of points.

1. $(2, 1), (8, 9)$

2. $(4, 9), (1, 6)$

3. $(7, -8), (14, -6)$

4. $(-10, 7), (-20, 8)$

5. $(3, 11), (-12, 18)$

6. $(-4, -1), (-2, -5)$

Determine the value of r so the line that passes through each pair of points has the given slope.

7. $(10, r), (3, 4), m = -\dfrac{2}{7}$

8. $(-1, -3), (7, r), m = \dfrac{3}{4}$

9. $(-2, r), (10, 4), m = -\dfrac{1}{2}$

10. $(12, r), (r, 6), m = 2$

11. $(6, 8), (r, -2), m = -3$

12. $(r, 9), (7, 5), m = 6$

Study Guide

Slope

The ratio of *rise* to *run* is called **slope**. The slope of a line describes its steepness, or rate of change.

On a coordinate plane, a line extending from lower left to upper right has a positive slope. A line extending from upper left to lower right has a negative slope. The slope of a horizontal line is zero. A vertical line has *no slope*.

The slope of a nonvertical line can be determined from the coordinates of any two points on the line.

Definition of Slope
The slope m of a line is the ratio of the change in the y-coordinates to the corresponding change in the x-coordinates. $\text{Slope} = \dfrac{\text{change in } y}{\text{change in } x}$ or $m = \dfrac{\text{change in } y}{\text{change in } x}$

Determining Slope Given Two Points
Given the coordinates of two points, (x_1, y_1) and (x_2, y_2), on a line, the slope m can be found as follows: $m = \dfrac{y_2 - y_1}{x_2 - x_1}$, where $x_1 \neq x_2$.

Example: Determine the slope of the line that passes through $(-1, 5)$ and $(4, -2)$.

$$m = \frac{y_2 - y_1}{x_2 - x_1}$$

$$= \frac{-2 - 5}{4 - (-1)}$$

$$= \frac{-7}{5} = -\frac{7}{5}$$

Determine the slope of the line that passes through each pair of points.

1. $(2, 1), (8, 9)$ $\dfrac{4}{3}$

2. $(4, 9), (1, 6)$ **1**

3. $(7, -8), (14, -6)$ $\dfrac{2}{7}$

4. $(-10, 7), (-20, 8)$ $-\dfrac{1}{10}$

5. $(3, 11), (-12, 18)$ $-\dfrac{7}{15}$

6. $(-4, -1), (-2, -5)$ -2

Determine the value of r so the line that passes through each pair of points has the given slope.

7. $(10, r), (3, 4), m = -\dfrac{2}{7}$ **2**

8. $(-1, -3), (7, r), m = \dfrac{3}{4}$ **3**

9. $(-2, r), (10, 4),$ $m = -\dfrac{1}{2}$ **10**

10. $(12, r), (r, 6), m = 2$ **10**

11. $(6, 8), (r, -2), m = -3$ $\dfrac{28}{3}$

12. $(r, 9), (7, 5), m = 6$ $\dfrac{23}{3}$

Study Guide

Writing Linear Equations in Point-Slope and Standard Forms

If you know the slope of a line and the coordinates of one point on the line, you can write an equation of the line by using the **point-slope form.** For a given point (x_1, y_1) on a nonvertical line with slope m, the point-slope form of a linear equation is $y - y_1 = m(x - x_1)$.

> Any linear equation can be expressed in the form $Ax + By = C$ where A, B, and C are integers and A and B are not both zero. This is called the **standard form.** An equation that is written in point-slope form can be changed to standard form.

Example 1: Write the point-slope form of an equation of the line that passes through $(6, 1)$ and has a slope of $-\dfrac{5}{2}$.

$$y - y_1 = m(x - x_1)$$
$$y - 1 = -\frac{5}{2}(x - 6)$$

Example 2: Write $y + 5 = 3(x - 4)$ in standard form.

$$y + 5 = 3(x - 4)$$
$$y + 5 = 3x - 12$$
$$-3x + y = -17$$
$$3x - y = 17$$

You can also find an equation of a line if you know the coordinates of two points on the line. First, find the slope of the line. Then write an equation of the line by using the point-slope form or the standard form.

Write the standard form of an equation of the line that passes through the given point and has the given slope.

1. $(2, 1)$, 4

2. $(-7, 2)$, 6

3. $\left(\dfrac{1}{2}, 3\right)$, 5

4. $(4, 9)$, $\dfrac{3}{4}$

5. $(-6, 7)$, 0

6. $(8, 3)$, 1

Write the point-slope form of an equation of the line that passes through each pair of points.

7. $(6, 3)$, $(-8, 5)$

8. $(-1, 9)$, $(10, 7)$

9. $(8, 5)$, $(0, -4)$

10. $(-3, -4)$, $(5, -6)$

11. $(2, 9)$, $(9, 2)$

12. $(-1, -4)$, $(-6, -10)$

NAME_____ DATE _____

Study Guide

Writing Linear Equations in Point-Slope and Standard Forms

If you know the slope of a line and the coordinates of one point on the line, you can write an equation of the line by using the **point-slope form.** For a given point (x_1, y_1) on a nonvertical line with slope m, the point-slope form of a linear equation is $y - y_1 = m(x - x_1)$.

> Any linear equation can be expressed in the form $Ax + By = C$ where A, B, and C are integers and A and B are not both zero. This is called the **standard form.** An equation that is written in point-slope form can be changed to standard form.

Example 1: Write the point-slope form of an equation of the line that passes through $(6, 1)$ and has a slope of $-\dfrac{5}{2}$.

$$y - y_1 = m(x - x_1)$$
$$y - 1 = -\frac{5}{2}(x - 6)$$

Example 2: Write $y + 5 = 3(x - 4)$ in standard form.

$$y + 5 = 3(x - 4)$$
$$y + 5 = 3x - 12$$
$$-3x + y = -17$$
$$3x - y = 17$$

You can also find an equation of a line if you know the coordinates of two points on the line. First, find the slope of the line. Then write an equation of the line by using the point-slope form or the standard form.

Write the standard form of an equation of the line that passes through the given point and has the given slope.

1. $(2, 1), 4$
   $4x - y = 7$

2. $(-7, 2), 6$
   $6x - y = -44$

3. $\left(\frac{1}{2}, 3\right), 5$
   $10x - 2y = -1$

4. $(4, 9), \dfrac{3}{4}$
   $3x - 4y = -24$

5. $(-6, 7), 0$
   $y = 7$

6. $(8, 3), 1$
   $x - y = 5$

Write the point-slope form of an equation of the line that passes through each pair of points.

7. $(6, 3), (-8, 5)$
   $y - 3 = -\frac{1}{7}(x - 6)$

8. $(-1, 9), (10, 7)$
   $y - 7 = -\frac{2}{11}(x - 10)$

9. $(8, 5), (0, -4)$
   $y - 5 = \frac{9}{8}(x - 8)$

10. $(-3, -4), (5, -6)$
    $y + 6 = -\frac{1}{4}(x - 5)$

11. $(2, 9), (9, 2)$
    $y - 2 = -(x - 9)$

12. $(-1, -4), (-6, -10)$
    $y + 10 = \frac{6}{5}(x + 6)$

NAME_____ DATE _____

Study Guide

Integration: Statistics
Scatter Plots and Best-Fit Lines

A **scatter plot** is a graph that shows the relationship between paired data. The scatter plot may reveal a pattern, or association, between the paired data. This association can be negative or positive. The association is said to be positive when a line suggested by the points slants upward.

The scatter plot at the right represents the relationship between the amount of money Carmen earned each week and the amount she deposited to her savings account. Since the points suggest a line that slants upward, there seems to be a positive relationship between the paired data. In general, the scatter plot seems to show that the more Carmen earned, the more she saved.

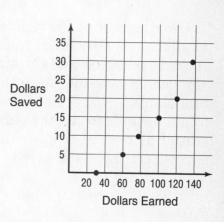

Solve each problem.

1. The table below shows the number of bull's-eyes attempted and the number of bull's-eyes made during a few dart games.

   a. Draw a scatter plot at the right from the data in the table.

Bull's-eyes		
Name	**Attempted**	**Made**
Darlene	5	4
Chris	7	7
Mark	5	1
Kathy	6	2

   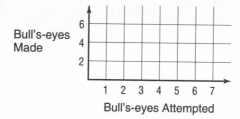

   b. What are the paired data?

   c. Is there a relationship between attempts and successes?

2. Anna's running speed after 5 minutes was 10 mi/h; at 10 minutes, 8 mi/h; at 15 minutes, 5 mi/h; and at 20 minutes, 4 mi/h.

   a. Make a scatter plot pairing time run with running speed.

   b. How is the data related, positively, negatively, or not at all?

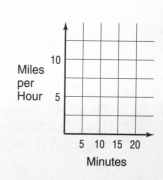

Study Guide

Integration: Statistics
Scatter Plots and Best-Fit Lines

A **scatter plot** is a graph that shows the relationship between paired data. The scatter plot may reveal a pattern, or association, between the paired data. This association can be negative or positive. The association is said to be positive when a line suggested by the points slants upward.

The scatter plot at the right represents the relationship between the amount of money Carmen earned each week and the amount she deposited to her savings account. Since the points suggest a line that slants upward, there seems to be a positive relationship between the paired data. In general, the scatter plot seems to show that the more Carmen earned, the more she saved.

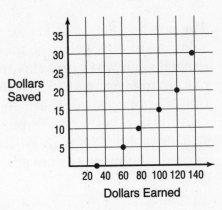

Solve each problem.

1. The table below shows the number of bull's-eyes attempted and the number of bull's-eyes made during a few dart games.

   a. Draw a scatter plot at the right from the data in the table.

Bull's-eyes		
Name	**Attempted**	**Made**
Darlene	5	4
Chris	7	7
Mark	5	1
Kathy	6	2

   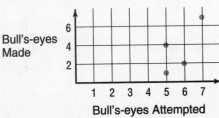

   b. What are the paired data?
   the number of bull's-eyes attempted and the number of bull's-eyes made

   c. Is there a relationship between attempts and successes?
   There is a weak suggestion of a positive correlation.

2. Anna's running speed after 5 minutes was 10 mi/h; at 10 minutes, 8 mi/h; at 15 minutes, 5 mi/h; and at 20 minutes, 4 mi/h.

   a. Make a scatter plot pairing time run with running speed.

   b. How is the data related, positively, negatively, or not at all? **negatively**

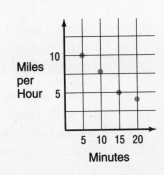

Study Guide

Writing Linear Equations in Slope-Intercept Form

The x-coordinate of the point where a line crosses the x-axis is called the **x-intercept.** Similarly, the y-coordinate of the point where the line crosses the y-axis is called the **y-intercept.**

Slope-Intercept Form of a Linear Equation
Given the slope m and the y-intercept b of a line, the slope-intercept form of an equation of the line is
$y = mx + b.$

If an equation is given in standard form $Ax + By = C$ and B is not zero, the slope of the line is $-\dfrac{A}{B}$ and the y-intercept is $\dfrac{C}{B}$. The x-intercept is $\dfrac{C}{A}$ where $A \neq 0$.

Example: Find the x- and y-intercepts of the graph of $5x - 2y = 10$. Then write the equation in slope-intercept form.

Since $A = 5$, $B = -2$, and $C = 10$,

$$\frac{C}{A} = \frac{10}{5} \qquad \frac{C}{B} = \frac{10}{-2} \qquad m = -\frac{A}{B}$$

$$= 2 \qquad\qquad = -5 \qquad\qquad = \frac{5}{2}$$

Thus, the x-intercept is 2, and the y-intercept is -5. The equation of the line in slope-intercept form is

$$y = \frac{5}{2}x - 5.$$

Find the x- and y-intercepts of the graph of each equation.

1. $5x + 4y = 20$

2. $2x - 5y = -7$

3. $4x - 8y = 10$

4. $9x + y = -1$

Write an equation in slope-intercept form of a line with the given slope and y-intercept. Then write the equation in standard form.

5. $m = 6, b = 10$

6. $m = 4, b = 0$

7. $m = -1, b = 3$

8. $m = 2, b = -3$

Find the slope and y-intercept of the graph of each equation. Then write each equation in slope-intercept form.

9. $0.2x + 0.5y = 1.6$

10. $3x + 7y = 10$

11. $6x - y = 9$

12. $14x - 21y = 7$

Writing Linear Equations in Slope-Intercept Form

The x-coordinate of the point where a line crosses the x-axis is called the **x-intercept.** Similarly, the y-coordinate of the point where the line crosses the y-axis is called the **y-intercept.**

Slope-Intercept Form of a Linear Equation
Given the slope m and the y-intercept b of a line, the slope-intercept form of an equation of the line is $y = mx + b$.

If an equation is given in standard form $Ax + By = C$ and B is not zero, the slope of the line is $-\frac{A}{B}$ and the y-intercept is $\frac{C}{B}$. The x-intercept is $\frac{C}{A}$ where $A \neq 0$.

Example: Find the x- and y-intercepts of the graph of $5x - 2y = 10$. Then write the equation in slope-intercept form.

Since $A = 5$, $B = -2$, and $C = 10$,

$$\frac{C}{A} = \frac{10}{5} \qquad \frac{C}{B} = \frac{10}{-2} \qquad m = -\frac{A}{B}$$

$$= 2 \qquad\qquad = -5 \qquad\qquad = \frac{5}{2}$$

Thus, the x-intercept is 2, and the y-intercept is -5. The equation of the line in slope-intercept form is

$$y = \frac{5}{2}x - 5.$$

Find the x- and y-intercepts of the graph of each equation.

1. $5x + 4y = 20$ **4, 5**

2. $2x - 5y = -7$ $-\dfrac{7}{2}, \dfrac{7}{5}$

3. $4x - 8y = 10$ $\dfrac{5}{2}, -\dfrac{5}{4}$

4. $9x + y = -1$ $-\dfrac{1}{9}, -1$

Write an equation in slope-intercept form of a line with the given slope and y-intercept. Then write the equation in standard form.

5. $m = 6, b = 10$ **$y = 6x + 10$;**
   $6x - y = -10$

6. $m = 4, b = 0$ **$y = 4x$;**
   $4x - y = 0$

7. $m = -1, b = 3$ **$y = -x + 3$;**
   $x + y = 3$

8. $m = 2, b = -3$ **$y = 2x - 3$;**
   $2x - y = 3$

Find the slope and y-intercept of the graph of each equation. Then write each equation in slope-intercept form.

9. $0.2x + 0.5y = 1.6$
   $-\dfrac{2}{5}, \dfrac{16}{5}; \; y = -\dfrac{2}{5}x + \dfrac{16}{5}$

10. $3x + 7y = 10$
    $-\dfrac{3}{7}, \dfrac{10}{7}; \; y = -\dfrac{3}{7}x + \dfrac{10}{7}$

11. $6x - y = 9$
    $6; -9; \; y = 6x - 9$

12. $14x - 21y = 7$
    $\dfrac{2}{3}, -\dfrac{1}{3}; \; y = \dfrac{2}{3}x - \dfrac{1}{3}$

Study Guide

Graphing Linear Equations

There are three methods you can use for graphing equations. You can find two ordered pairs that satisfy the equation, the x- and y-intercepts, or the slope and y-intercept.

Example 1: Graph $5x + 4y = 20$ by using the x- and y-intercepts.

The equation is in standard form $Ax + By = C$.

The x-intercept is $\dfrac{C}{A}$, or 4.

The y-intercept is $\dfrac{C}{B}$, or 5.

Thus, the graph contains the points (4, 0) and (0, 5).

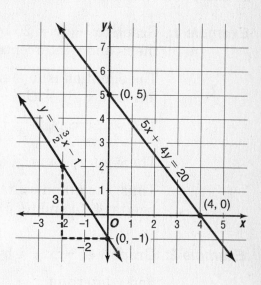

Example 2: Graph $y = -\dfrac{3}{2}x - 1$ by using the slope and y-intercept.

The y-intercept is -1, the slope $-\dfrac{3}{2}$.

Graph each equation by using the x- and y-intercepts.

1. $-3x + 2y = 6$

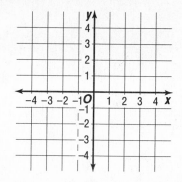

2. $3y + x = 3$

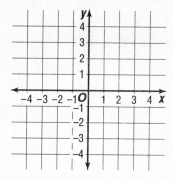

Graph each equation by using the slope and y-intercept.

3. $y = \dfrac{1}{3}x + 2$

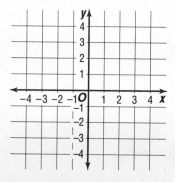

4. $y = \dfrac{1}{2}x + \dfrac{3}{4}$

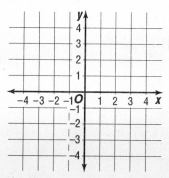

6-5

Study Guide

Graphing Linear Equations

There are three methods you can use for graphing equations. You can find two ordered pairs that satisfy the equation, the x- and y-intercepts, or the slope and y-intercept.

Example 1: Graph $5x + 4y = 20$ by using the x- and y-intercepts.

The equation is in standard form $Ax + By = C$.

The x-intercept is $\frac{C}{A}$, or 4.

The y-intercept is $\frac{C}{B}$, or 5.

Thus, the graph contains the points (4, 0) and (0, 5).

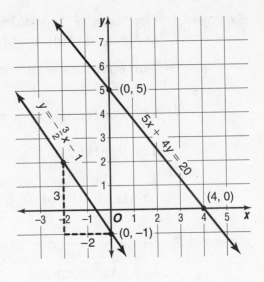

Example 2: Graph $y = -\frac{3}{2}x - 1$ by using the slope and y-intercept.

The y-intercept is −1, the slope $-\frac{3}{2}$.

Graph each equation by using the x- and y-intercepts.

1. $-3x + 2y = 6$

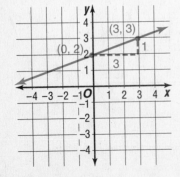

2. $3y + x = 3$

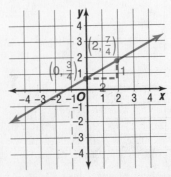

Graph each equation by using the slope and y-intercept.

3. $y = \frac{1}{3}x + 2$

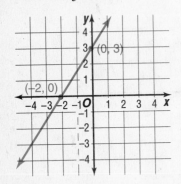

4. $y = \frac{1}{2}x + \frac{3}{4}$

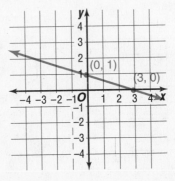

Study Guide

Integration: Geometry
Parallel and Perpendicular Lines

When you graph two lines, you may encounter the two special types of graphs described at the right.

Parallel Lines and Perpendicular Lines
If two nonvertical lines have the same slope, then they are **parallel.** All vertical lines are parallel.
If the product of the slope of two lines is −1, then the lines are **perpendicular.** In a plane, vertical lines and horizontal lines are perpendicular.

Example: Write an equation in slope-intercept form of the line that passes through $(0, 6)$ and is parallel to the graph of $2x - y = -12$.

The slope of the graph is 2. $-\dfrac{A}{B} = -\dfrac{2}{-1}$, or 2

The slope-intercept form of an equation whose graph is parallel to the original graph is $y = 2x + b$.
Substitute $(0, 6)$ into the equation and solve for b.
$$6 = 0x + b$$
$$b = 6 \qquad \text{The } y\text{-intercept is } b.$$

The equation of the line is $y = 2x + 6$.

Since $2 \cdot \left(-\dfrac{1}{2}\right) = -1$, any line that is perpendicular to the line in the Example has an equation of the form $y = -\dfrac{1}{2}x + b$. If the line includes the point $(-4, 3)$, then $3 = -\dfrac{1}{2}(-4) + b$ and thus $b = 1$. The equation of the line is $y = -\dfrac{1}{2}x + 1$.

Write an equation in slope-intercept form of the line that passes through the given point and is parallel to the graph of each equation.

1. $y = -\dfrac{2}{3}x + 4;\ (1, -3)$ 2. $y = \dfrac{1}{2}x + 1;\ (4, 2)$ 3. $2x + y = 5;\ (4, -6)$

4. $3x - y = 0;\ (7, 2)$ 5. $x - 8y = 10;\ (0, 5)$ 6. $7x + 2y = 3;\ (1, 6)$

Write an equation in slope-intercept form of the line that passes through the given point and is perpendicular to the graph of each equation.

7. $4x - 3y = 7;\ (5, -2)$ 8. $6x + 16y = 8;\ (0, 4)$ 9. $y = 7x + 1;\ (6, 4)$

Study Guide

Integration: Geometry
Parallel and Perpendicular Lines

When you graph two lines, you may encounter the two special types of graphs described at the right.

Parallel Lines and Perpendicular Lines
If two nonvertical lines have the same slope, then they are **parallel**. All vertical lines are parallel.
If the product of the slope of two lines is −1, then the lines are **perpendicular**. In a plane, vertical lines and horizontal lines are perpendicular.

Example: Write an equation in slope-intercept form of the line that passes through $(0, 6)$ and is parallel to the graph of $2x - y = -12$.

The slope of the graph is 2. $-\dfrac{A}{B} = -\dfrac{2}{-1}$, or 2

The slope-intercept form of an equation whose graph is parallel to the original graph is $y = 2x + b$.
Substitute $(0, 6)$ into the equation and solve for b.
$$6 = 0x + b$$
$$b = 6 \qquad \text{The y-intercept is } b.$$

The equation of the line is $y = 2x + 6$.

Since $2 \cdot \left(-\dfrac{1}{2}\right) = -1$, any line that is perpendicular to the line in the Example has an equation of the form $y = -\dfrac{1}{2}x + b$. If the line includes the point $(-4, 3)$, then $3 = -\dfrac{1}{2}(-4) + b$ and thus $b = 1$. The equation of the line is $y = -\dfrac{1}{2}x + 1$.

Write an equation in slope-intercept form of the line that passes through the given point and is parallel to the graph of each equation.

1. $y = -\dfrac{2}{3}x + 4$; $(1, -3)$
   $y = -\dfrac{2}{3}x - \dfrac{7}{3}$

2. $y = \dfrac{1}{2}x + 1$; $(4, 2)$
   $y = \dfrac{1}{2}x$

3. $2x + y = 5$; $(4, -6)$
   $y = -2x + 2$

4. $3x - y = 0$; $(7, 2)$
   $y = 3x - 19$

5. $x - 8y = 10$; $(0, 5)$
   $y = \dfrac{1}{8}x + 5$

6. $7x + 2y = 3$; $(1, 6)$
   $y = -\dfrac{7}{2}x + \dfrac{19}{2}$

Write an equation in slope-intercept form of the line that passes through the given point and is perpendicular to the graph of each equation.

7. $4x - 3y = 7$; $(5, -2)$
   $y = -\dfrac{3}{4}x + \dfrac{7}{4}$

8. $6x + 16y = 8$; $(0, 4)$
   $y = \dfrac{8}{3}x + 4$

9. $y = 7x + 1$; $(6, 4)$
   $y = -\dfrac{1}{7}x + \dfrac{34}{7}$

Algebra 1

Study Guide

Integration: Geometry
Midpoint of a Line Segment

The **midpoint** of a line segment is the point that is halfway between the endpoints of the segment.

Midpoint of a Line Segment
The coordinates of the midpoint of a line segment whose endpoints are at (x_1, y_1) and (x_2, y_2) are given by $\left(\dfrac{x_1 + x_2}{2}, \dfrac{y_1 + y_2}{2}\right)$.

Example: Find the coordinates of the midpoint of a segment whose endpoints are $F(-4, 5)$ and $G(6, -1)$.

$$(x, y) = \left(\frac{x_1 + x_2}{2}, \frac{y_1 + y_2}{2}\right)$$
$$= \left(\frac{-4 + 6}{2}, \frac{5 + (-1)}{2}\right)$$
$$= (1, 2)$$

The coordinates of the midpoint of $\overline{FG}$ are $(1, 2)$.

Find the coordinates of the midpoint of a segment with each pair of endpoints.

1. $C(6, 2), D(4, 1)$

2. $M(5, 7), N(3, 9)$

3. $I(0, -2), J\left(\frac{3}{4}, 5\right)$

4. $K\left(\frac{1}{4}, 1\right), L\left(\frac{1}{8}, 0\right)$

5. $G(10, -8), H(4, -3)$

6. $A(6, 5), B(3, -1)$

7. $E(2, 7), F(8, 4)$

8. $R(13, 10), S(7, 27)$

9. $P(x, y), Q(3x, 5y)$

If P is the midpoint of segment AB, find the coordinates of the missing point.

10. $A(4, 1), B(6, 3)$

11. $B(-14, 24), P(-2, 7)$

12. $B(-8, -10), P(-9, 0)$

13. $A(11, 12), P(2, 17)$

14. $A(9, -18), B(5, -16)$

15. $B(0, 12), P(-5, -1)$

Algebra 1

Integration: Geometry
Midpoint of a Line Segment

The **midpoint** of a line segment is the point that is halfway between the endpoints of the segment.

> **Midpoint of a Line Segment**
>
> The coordinates of the midpoint of a line segment whose endpoints are at (x_1, y_1) and (x_2, y_2) are given by $\left(\dfrac{x_1 + x_2}{2}, \dfrac{y_1 + y_2}{2}\right)$.

Example: Find the coordinates of the midpoint of a segment whose endpoints are $F(-4, 5)$ and $G(6, -1)$.

$$(x, y) = \left(\frac{x_1 + x_2}{2}, \frac{y_1 + y_2}{2}\right)$$
$$= \left(\frac{-4 + 6}{2}, \frac{5 + (-1)}{2}\right)$$
$$= (1, 2)$$

The coordinates of the midpoint of $\overline{FG}$ are $(1, 2)$.

Find the coordinates of the midpoint of a segment with each pair of endpoints.

1. $C(6, 2), D(4, 1)$
$\left(5, \dfrac{3}{2}\right)$

2. $M(5, 7), N(3, 9)$
(4, 8)

3. $I(0, -2), J\left(\dfrac{3}{4}, 5\right)$
$\left(\dfrac{3}{8}, \dfrac{3}{2}\right)$

4. $K\left(\dfrac{1}{4}, 1\right), L\left(\dfrac{1}{8}, 0\right)$
$\left(\dfrac{3}{16}, \dfrac{1}{2}\right)$

5. $G(10, -8), H(4, -3)$
$\left(7, -\dfrac{11}{2}\right)$

6. $A(6, 5), B(3, -1)$
$\left(\dfrac{9}{2}, 2\right)$

7. $E(2, 7), F(8, 4)$
$\left(5, \dfrac{11}{2}\right)$

8. $R(13, 10), S(7, 27)$
$\left(10, \dfrac{37}{2}\right)$

9. $P(x, y), Q(3x, 5y)$
(2x, 3y)

If P is the midpoint of segment AB, find the coordinates of the missing point.

10. $A(4, 1), B(6, 3)$
P(5, 2)

11. $B(-14, 24), P(-2, 7)$
A(10, -10)

12. $B(-8, -10), P(-9, 0)$
A(-10, 10)

13. $A(11, 12), P(2, 17)$
B(-7, 22)

14. $A(9, -18), B(5, -16)$
P(7, -17)

15. $B(0, 12), P(-5, -1)$
A(-10, -14)

Solving Inequalities by Using Addition and Subtraction

You can use the addition and subtraction properties for inequalities when solving problems involving inequalities.

Addition and Subtraction Properties for Inequalities
For all numbers *a*, *b*, and *c*,
1. if $a > b$, then $a + c > b + c$ and $a - c > b - c$;
2. if $a < b$, then $a + c < b + c$ and $a - c < b - c$.

Example: Solve $3a + 5 > 4 + 2a$.

$$3a + 5 > 4 + 2a$$
$$3a - 2a + 5 > 4 + 2a - 2a$$
$$a + 5 > 4$$
$$a + 5 - 5 > 4 - 5$$
$$a > -1$$

The solution set is {all numbers greater than -1}.

To check your solution, choose two numbers, one greater than -1, and one less than -1. Substitute both numbers in the original inequality. Only those numbers greater than -1 should yield a true statement.

The solution set in the above example, written in set-builder notation is $\{a \mid a > -1\}$. This is read "The set of all numbers a such that a is greater than -1."

Solve each inequality. Then check your solution.

1. $a + 4 < 14$

2. $9k - 12 > 80 + 8k$

3. $-19 + x < 2x - 33$

4. $6y > 14 - 2 + 7y$

5. $3n + 17 < 4n - 6$

6. $\frac{3}{2}q - \frac{25}{5} \geq \frac{2q}{4}$

7. $h + \frac{2}{3} \leq 2 - \frac{2}{3}$

8. $4p - 3.2 \geq 3p + 0.7$

9. $-2\frac{1}{2}z \leq 3\frac{1}{3} + 2\frac{1}{3} - 3\frac{1}{2}z$

10. $\frac{1}{b} + 4 \leq 10 + \frac{1}{b}, b \neq 0$

11. $6r > 10r - r - 3r$

12. $3.2x < 2x - (9 - 1.2x)$

Study Guide

Solving Inequalities by Using Addition and Subtraction

You can use the addition and subtraction properties for inequalities when solving problems involving inequalities.

Addition and Subtraction Properties for Inequalities
For all numbers a, b, and c,   1. if $a > b$, then $a + c > b + c$ and $a - c > b - c$;   2. if $a < b$, then $a + c < b + c$ and $a - c < b - c$.

Example: Solve $3a + 5 > 4 + 2a$.

$$3a + 5 > 4 + 2a$$
$$3a - 2a + 5 > 4 + 2a - 2a$$
$$a + 5 > 4$$
$$a + 5 - 5 > 4 - 5$$
$$a > -1$$

The solution set is {all numbers greater than -1}.

To check your solution, choose two numbers, one greater than -1, and one less than -1. Substitute both numbers in the original inequality. Only those numbers greater than -1 should yield a true statement.

The solution set in the above example, written in set-builder notation is $\{a \mid a > -1\}$. This is read "The set of all numbers a such that a is greater than -1."

Solve each inequality. Then check your solution.

1. $a + 4 < 14$
   $\{a \mid a < 10\}$

2. $9k - 12 > 80 + 8k$
   $\{k \mid k > 92\}$

3. $-19 + x < 2x - 33$
   $\{x \mid x > 14\}$

4. $6y > 14 - 2 + 7y$
   $\{y \mid y < -12\}$

5. $3n + 17 < 4n - 6$
   $\{n \mid n > 23\}$

6. $\frac{3}{2}q - \frac{25}{5} \geq \frac{2q}{4}$
   $\{q \mid q \geq 5\}$

7. $h + \frac{2}{3} \leq 2 - \frac{2}{3}$
   $\left\{h \mid h \leq \frac{2}{3}\right\}$

8. $4p - 3.2 \geq 3p + 0.7$
   $\{p \mid p \geq 3.9\}$

9. $-2\frac{1}{2}z \leq 3\frac{1}{3} + 2\frac{1}{3} - 3\frac{1}{2}z$
   $\left\{z \mid z \leq 5\frac{2}{3}\right\}$

10. $\frac{1}{b} + 4 \leq 10 + \frac{1}{b}$, $b \neq 0$
    all numbers

11. $6r > 10r - r - 3r$
    no solution

12. $3.2x < 2x - (9 - 1.2x)$
    no solution

NAME_____ DATE _____

Study Guide

Student Edition
Pages 392–398

Solving Inequalities by Using Multiplication and Division

You can solve inequalities by using the same methods you have already used to solve equations. However, when solving inequalities, if you multiply or divide each side by the same negative number, you must *reverse* the direction of the inequality symbol. The following chart shows the multiplication and division properties for solving inequalities.

Multiplication Property for Inequalities	Division Property for Inequalities

For all numbers a, b, and c,
 1. if c is positive and $a < b$, then $ac < bc$;
 	
    if c is positive and $a > b$, then $ac > bc$;
 	
 2. if c is negative and $a < b$, then $ac > bc$;
 	
    if c is negative and $a > b$, then $ac < bc$.
	For all numbers a, b, and c,
	 1. if c is positive and $a < b$, then $\frac{a}{c} < \frac{b}{c}$;
	
	    if c is positive and $a > b$, then $\frac{a}{c} > \frac{b}{c}$;
	
	 2. if c is negative and $a < b$, then $\frac{a}{c} > \frac{b}{c}$;
	
	    if c is negative and $a > b$, then $\frac{a}{c} < \frac{b}{c}$.

State the number by which you multiply each side to solve each inequality. Indicate whether the direction of the inequality symbol reverses.

1. $4s < 24$ 2. $-9k > 2$ 3. $-5\frac{1}{3} > 2n$ 4. $\frac{7}{3} < -\frac{1}{9}n$

Solve each inequality. Then check your solution.

5. $77 < 12r$ 6. $-5c > 2$ 7. $25g \geq -100$ 8. $\frac{n}{-50} > 22$

9. $0.24 < 0.6w$ 10. $-2.51 \leq \frac{2h}{-4}$ 11. $\frac{2a}{7} \geq -6$ 12. $-\frac{1}{3} < \frac{2p}{9}$

Define a variable, write an inequality, and solve each problem. Then check your solution.

13. Four times a number is no more than 108.

14. A number divided by 5 is at least −10.

Study Guide

Solving Inequalities by Using Multiplication and Division

You can solve inequalities by using the same methods you have already used to solve equations. However, when solving inequalities, if you multiply or divide each side by the same negative number, you must *reverse* the direction of the inequality symbol. The following chart shows the multiplication and division properties for solving inequalities.

Multiplication Property for Inequalities	Division Property for Inequalities
For all numbers a, b, and c, 1. if c is positive and $a < b$, then $ac < bc$; if c is positive and $a > b$, then $ac > bc$; 2. if c is negative and $a < b$, then $ac > bc$; if c is negative and $a > b$, then $ac < bc$.	For all numbers a, b, and c, 1. if c is positive and $a < b$, then $\dfrac{a}{c} < \dfrac{b}{c}$; if c is positive and $a > b$, then $\dfrac{a}{c} > \dfrac{b}{c}$; 2. if c is negative and $a < b$, then $\dfrac{a}{c} > \dfrac{b}{c}$; if c is negative and $a > b$, then $\dfrac{a}{c} < \dfrac{b}{c}$.

State the number by which you multiply each side to solve each inequality. Indicate whether the direction of the inequality symbol reverses.

1. $4s < 24$
$\frac{1}{4}$; no

2. $-9k > 2$
$-\frac{1}{9}$; yes

3. $-5\frac{1}{3} > 2n$
$\frac{1}{2}$; no

4. $\frac{7}{3} < -\frac{1}{9}n$
-9; yes

Solve each inequality. Then check your solution.

5. $77 < 12r$
$\left\{ r \mid r > 6\frac{5}{12} \right\}$

6. $-5c > 2$
$\left\{ c \mid c < -\frac{2}{5} \right\}$

7. $25g \geq -100$
$\{g \mid g \geq -4\}$

8. $\frac{n}{-50} > 22$
$\{n \mid n < -1100\}$

9. $0.24 < 0.6w$
$\{w \mid w > 0.4\}$

10. $-2.51 \leq \frac{2h}{-4}$
$\{h \mid h \leq 5.02\}$

11. $\frac{2a}{7} \geq -6$
$\{a \mid a \geq -21\}$

12. $-\frac{1}{3} < \frac{2p}{9}$
$\left\{ p \mid p > -\frac{3}{2} \right\}$

Define a variable, write an inequality, and solve each problem. Then check your solution.

13. Four times a number is no more than 108.
$4n \leq 108$; $\{n \mid n \leq 27\}$

14. A number divided by 5 is at least -10.
$\frac{n}{5} \geq -10$; $\{n \mid n \geq -50\}$

NAME_____ DATE _____

Study Guide

Solving Multi-Step Inequalities

Solving an inequality may require more than one operation. Use the same procedure you used for solving equations to solve inequalities.

Procedure For Solving Inequalities
1. Use the distributive property to remove any grouping symbols.
2. Simplify each side of the inequality.
3. Undo any indicated additions and subtractions.
4. Undo any indicated multiplications and divisions involving the variable.

Example: Solve $21 > -7(m + 2)$.

$$21 > -7(m + 2)$$
$$21 > -7m - 14 \qquad \text{Use the distributive property.}$$
$$21 + 14 > -7m - 14 + 14 \qquad \text{Subtraction is indicated; use addition.}$$
$$35 > -7m$$
$$\frac{35}{-7} < \frac{-7m}{-7} \qquad \text{Multiplication is indicated; use division.}$$
$$\qquad\qquad\qquad \text{Reverse the inequality symbol.}$$
$$-5 < m$$

The solution set is $\{m \mid -5 < m\}$, or $\{m \mid m > -5\}$.

Solve each inequality. Then check your solution.

1. $11y + 13 \geq -1$

2. $-3v + 3 \leq -12$

3. $\frac{q}{7} + 1 > -5$

4. $-1 - \frac{m}{4} \leq 5$

5. $\frac{3x}{7} - 2 < -3$

6. $\frac{4x - 2}{5} \geq -4$

7. $9n - 24n + 42 > 0$

8. $4.6(x - 3.4) \geq 5.1x$

9. $7.3y - 3.02 > 4.9y$

10. $6y + 10 > 8 - (y + 14)$

11. $m + 17 \leq -(4m - 13)$

12. $-5x - (2x + 3) \geq 1$

Algebra 1

Study Guide

Solving Multi-Step Inequalities

Solving an inequality may require more than one operation.
Use the same procedure you used for solving equations to
solve inequalities.

Procedure For Solving Inequalities
1. Use the distributive property to remove any grouping symbols.
2. Simplify each side of the inequality.
3. Undo any indicated additions and subtractions.
4. Undo any indicated multiplications and divisions involving the variable.

Example: Solve $21 > -7(m + 2)$.

$$21 > -7(m + 2)$$
$$21 > -7m - 14 \qquad \text{Use the distributive property.}$$
$$21 + 14 > -7m - 14 + 14 \qquad \text{Subtraction is indicated; use addition.}$$
$$35 > -7m$$
$$\frac{35}{-7} < \frac{-7m}{-7} \qquad \text{Multiplication is indicated; use division.}$$
$$\qquad\qquad\qquad \text{Reverse the inequality symbol.}$$
$$-5 < m$$

The solution set is $\{m \mid -5 < m\}$, or $\{m \mid m > -5\}$.

Solve each inequality. Then check your solution.

1. $11y + 13 \geq -1$

$$\left\{ y \mid y \geq -1\tfrac{3}{11} \right\}$$

2. $-3v + 3 \leq -12$

$$\{v \mid v \geq 5\}$$

3. $\frac{q}{7} + 1 > -5$

$$\{q \mid q > -42\}$$

4. $-1 - \frac{m}{4} \leq 5$

$$\{m \mid m \geq -24\}$$

5. $\frac{3x}{7} - 2 < -3$

$$\left\{ x \mid x < -2\tfrac{1}{3} \right\}$$

6. $\frac{4x - 2}{5} \geq -4$

$$\left\{ x \mid x \geq -4\tfrac{1}{2} \right\}$$

7. $9n - 24n + 42 > 0$

$$\left\{ n \mid n < 2\tfrac{4}{5} \right\}$$

8. $4.6(x - 3.4) \geq 5.1x$

$$\{x \mid x \leq -31.28\}$$

9. $7.3y - 3.02 > 4.9y$

$$\left\{ y \mid y > 1\tfrac{31}{120} \right\}$$

10. $6y + 10 > 8 - (y + 14)$

$$\left\{ y \mid y > -2\tfrac{2}{7} \right\}$$

11. $m + 17 \leq -(4m - 13)$

$$\left\{ m \mid m \leq -\tfrac{4}{5} \right\}$$

12. $-5x - (2x + 3) \geq 1$

$$\left\{ x \mid x \leq -\tfrac{4}{7} \right\}$$

NAME _____ DATE _____

Study Guide

Student Edition
Pages 405–412

Solving Compound Inequalities

A **compound inequality** consists of two inequalities that are connected by the words *and* or *or*. A compound inequality containing *and* is true only if *both* inequalities are true. Its graph is the **intersection** of the graphs of the two inequalities. A compound inequality containing *or* is true if one or more of the inequalities is true. Its graph is the **union** of the graphs of the two inequalities.

Example 1: $x > -3$ and $x \leq 4$

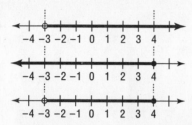

The solution set, shown in the bottom graph, is $\{x \mid -3 < x \leq 4\}$.

Example 2: $t \geq 8$ or $t < 5$

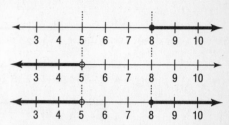

The solution set is $\{t \mid t \geq 8 \text{ or } t < 5\}$.

Sometimes it is better to first solve each inequality and then graph the solution. Study the examples below.

Example 3: $-3 \leq p - 5 < 2$

$$-3 \leq p - 5 \qquad \text{and} \qquad p - 5 < 2$$
$$-3 + 5 \leq p - 5 + 5 \qquad p - 5 + 5 < 2 + 5$$
$$2 \leq p \qquad\qquad\qquad p < 7$$

The solution set is $\{p \mid 2 \leq p < 7\}$.

Example 4: $2a + 1 < 11$ or $a > 3a + 2$

$$2a + 1 < 11 \qquad \text{or} \qquad a > 3a + 2$$
$$2a + 1 - 1 < 11 - 1 \qquad a - 3a > 3a - 3a + 2$$
$$2a < 10 \qquad\qquad -2a > 2$$
$$\frac{2a}{2} < \frac{10}{2} \qquad\qquad \frac{-2a}{-2} > \frac{2}{-2}$$
$$a < 5 \qquad\qquad a < -1$$

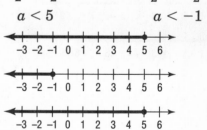

The solution set is $\{a \mid a \leq 5\}$.

Graph the solution set of each compound inequality.

1. $b > -1$ and $b \leq 3$

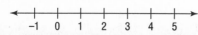

2. $y \leq -4$ or $y > 0$

3. $2 \geq q \geq -5$

Solve each compound inequality. Then graph the solution set.

4. $2x + 4 \leq 6$ or $x \geq 2x - 4$

5. $d - 3 < 6d + 12 < 2d + 32$

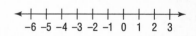

6. $4(g - 3) + 2 < 6$ and $7g > 3(2g - 1)$

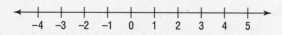

7. $3a + 2 \geq 5$ or $7 + 3a < 2(a + 3)$

51

Algebra 1

NAME_____ DATE_____

Study Guide

Student Edition
Pages 405–412

Solving Compound Inequalities

A **compound inequality** consists of two inequalities that are connected by the words *and* or *or*. A compound inequality containing *and* is true only if *both* inequalities are true. Its graph is the **intersection** of the graphs of the two inequalities. A compound inequality containing *or* is true if one or more of the inequalities is true. Its graph is the **union** of the graphs of the two inequalities.

Example 1: $x > -3$ and $x \leq 4$

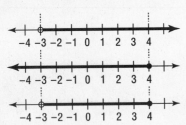

The solution set, shown in the bottom graph, is $\{x \mid -3 < x \leq 4\}$.

Example 2: $t \geq 8$ or $t < 5$

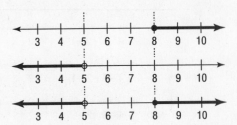

The solution set is $\{t \mid t \geq 8$ or $t < 5\}$.

Sometimes it is better to first solve each inequality and then graph the solution. Study the examples below.

Example 3: $-3 \leq p - 5 < 2$

$$-3 \leq p - 5 \qquad \text{and} \qquad p - 5 < 2$$
$$-3 + 5 \leq p - 5 + 5 \qquad p - 5 + 5 < 2 + 5$$
$$2 \leq p \qquad\qquad p < 7$$

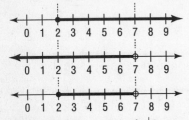

The solution set is $\{p \mid 2 \leq p < 7\}$.

Example 4: $2a + 1 < 11$ or $a > 3a + 2$

$$2a + 1 < 11 \qquad \text{or} \qquad a > 3a + 2$$
$$2a + 1 - 1 < 11 - 1 \qquad a - 3a > 3a - 3a + 2$$
$$2a < 10 \qquad\qquad -2a > 2$$
$$\frac{2a}{2} < \frac{10}{2} \qquad\qquad \frac{-2a}{-2} > \frac{2}{-2}$$
$$a < 5 \qquad\qquad a < -1$$

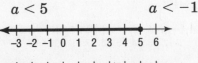

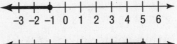

The solution set is $\{a \mid a \leq 5\}$.

Graph the solution set of each compound inequality.

1. $b > -1$ and $b \leq 3$

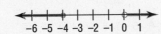

2. $y \leq -4$ or $y > 0$

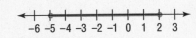

3. $2 \geq q \geq -5$

Solve each compound inequality. Then graph the solution set.

4. $2x + 4 \leq 6$ or $x \geq 2x - 4$

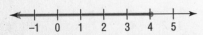

5. $d - 3 < 6d + 12 < 2d + 32$

6. $4(g - 3) + 2 < 6$ and $7g > 3(2g - 1)$

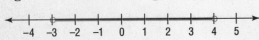

7. $3a + 2 \geq 5$ or $7 + 3a < 2(a + 3)$

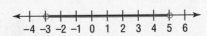

NAME_____ DATE_____

Study Guide

Integration: Probability
Compound Events

A **compound event** consists of two or more simple events. The probability of a compound event can be calculated if its outcomes are equally likely. To calculate probability, determine the possible outcomes. A tree diagram is a good way of doing this.

Example: A die is rolled and a coin is tossed. What is the probability of getting a three on the die and heads on the coin?

To calculate the probability, you need to know how many outcomes are possible. There are 12 possible outcomes. The probability of getting a three on the die and a heads on the coin is $\frac{1}{12}$.

```
1 < H
    T
2 < H
    T
3 < H
    T
4 < H
    T
5 < H
    T
6 < H
    T
```

Solve each problem.

1. Max makes three piles of cards, each consisting of only a Queen and a Jack. Lisa draws one card from each pile. What is the probability that Lisa draws two Queens and a Jack in any order? Make a tree diagram of all the choices.

2. Phyllis drops three pennies in a wishing pond. What is the probability that only one lands with tails showing? Make a tree diagram of all the choices.

3. George has 1 pair of red socks and 1 pair of white socks in a drawer. What is the probability of drawing 2 red socks?

4. In Exercise 3, what is the probability of picking a red sock and a white sock in that order.

NAME_____ DATE _____

Study Guide

Integration: Probability
Compound Events

A **compound event** consists of two or more simple events. The probability of a compound event can be calculated if its outcomes are equally likely. To calculate probability, determine the possible outcomes. A tree diagram is a good way of doing this.

Example: A die is rolled and a coin is tossed. What is the probability of getting a three on the die and heads on the coin?

To calculate the probability, you need to know how many outcomes are possible. There are 12 possible outcomes. The probability of getting a three on the die and a heads on the coin is $\frac{1}{12}$.

```
1 —< H
     T
2 —< H
     T
3 —< H
     T
4 —< H
     T
5 —< H
     T
6 —< H
     T
```

Solve each problem.

1. Max makes three piles of cards, each consisting of only a Queen and a Jack. Lisa draws one card from each pile. What is the probability that Lisa draws two Queens and a Jack in any order? Make a tree diagram of all the choices. $\frac{3}{8}$

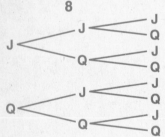

2. Phyllis drops three pennies in a wishing pond. What is the probability that only one lands with tails showing? Make a tree diagram of all the choices. $\frac{3}{8}$

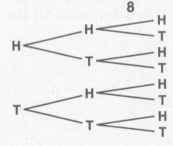

3. George has 1 pair of red socks and 1 pair of white socks in a drawer. What is the probability of drawing 2 red socks? $\frac{1}{6}$

4. In Exercise 3, what is the probability of picking a red sock and a white sock in that order. $\frac{1}{3}$

```
        R       R       W       W
       /|\     /|\     /|\     /|\
tree for Exercises 3 and 4:  R W W R W W R R W R R W
```

Algebra 1

NAME_____ DATE _____

Study Guide

Student Edition
Pages 420–426

Solving Open Sentences Involving Absolute Value

An open sentence involving absolute value should be interpreted, solved, and graphed as a compound sentence. Study the examples that follow.

Example 1:

$|5y - 2| = 7$ means
$5y - 2 = 7$ or $5y - 2 = -7$.
    $5y = 9$ $5y = -5$
      $y = 1\frac{4}{5}$ $y = 1$

Graph:

Example 2:

$|3a + 4| < 10$ means
$3a + 4 < 10$ and $3a + 4 > -10$.
   $3a < 6$ $3a > -14$
    $a < 2$ $a > -4\frac{2}{3}$

Graph: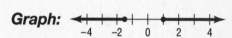

Example 3: $|4z + 1| \geq 5$ means
      $4z + 1 \leq -5$ or $4z + 1 \geq 5$.
        $4z \leq -6$ $4z \geq 4$
         $z \leq -1\frac{1}{2}$ $z \geq 1$ **Graph:**

Solve each open sentence. Then graph the solution set on the number line provided.

1. $|c - 2| > 6$

2. $|x - 9| < 0$

3. $|3f + 10| \leq 4$

*Express each statement in terms of an inequality involving absolute value. Do **not** try to solve.*

4. The price was within $10.00 of his $100.00 limit.

5. Her score was more than 20 points from the 53 point record.

6. The poll showed the incumbent mayor had the support of 12% of the voters plus or minus 3 percent points.

7. Mike swam his daily laps no more than 5 seconds off his previous record of 40 seconds.

For each graph, write an open sentence involving absolute value.

8.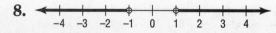

9.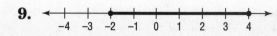

Solving Open Sentences Involving Absolute Value

An open sentence involving absolute value should be interpreted, solved, and graphed as a compound sentence. Study the examples that follow.

Example 1:

$|5y - 2| = 7$ means
$5y - 2 = 7$ or $5y - 2 = -7.$
$5y = 9$ $5y = -5$
$y = 1\frac{4}{5}$ $y = 1$

Graph:

Example 2:

$|3a + 4| < 10$ means
$3a + 4 < 10$ and $3a + 4 > -10.$
$3a < 6$ $3a > -14$
$a < 2$ $a > -4\frac{2}{3}$

Graph:

Example 3: $|4z + 1| \geq 5$ means
$4z + 1 \leq -5$ or $4z + 1 \geq 5.$
$4z \leq -6$ $4z \geq 4$
$z \leq -1\frac{1}{2}$ $z \geq 1$ **Graph:**

Solve each open sentence. Then graph the solution set on the number line provided.

1. $|c - 2| > 6$

$\{c \mid c < -4 \text{ or } c > 8\}$

2. $|x - 9| < 0$

no solution

3. $|3f + 10| \leq 4$

$\left\{f \mid -4\frac{2}{3} \leq f \leq -2\right\}$

Express each statement in terms of an inequality involving absolute value. Do _not_ try to solve.

4. The price was within $10.00 of his $100.00 limit. $|p - 100| < 10$

5. Her score was more than 20 points from the 53 point record.
$|s - 53| > 20$

6. The poll showed the incumbent mayor had the support of 12% of the voters plus or minus 3 percent points.
$|v - 0.12| \leq 0.03$

7. Mike swam his daily laps no more than 5 seconds off his previous record of 40 seconds. $|x - 40| \leq 5$

For each graph, write an open sentence involving absolute value.

8.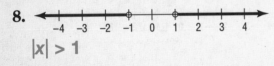

$|x| > 1$

9.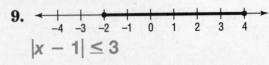

$|x - 1| \leq 3$

Study Guide

Student Edition
Pages 427–432

Integration: Statistics
Box-and-Whisker Plots

A box-and-whisker plot displays the extremes, the quartiles, and the median for a set of data. It may be drawn horizontally or vertically.

Study the box at the right. Note the dots marking the extremes, the quartiles, and the median.

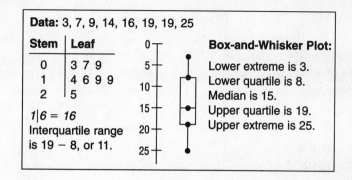

Data: 3, 7, 9, 14, 16, 19, 19, 25

Stem	Leaf
0	3 7 9
1	4 6 9 9
2	5

$1|6 = 16$
Interquartile range is 19 − 8, or 11.

Box-and-Whisker Plot:
Lower extreme is 3.
Lower quartile is 8.
Median is 15.
Upper quartile is 19.
Upper extreme is 25.

Answer each question for the indicated box-and-whisker plot.

1. What are the upper and lower extremes?

2. What is the median?

3. What are the upper and lower quartiles?

4. What is the interquartile range?

Use the data given to complete the following. **Data: 19, 49, 73, 30, 32, 46, 51, 30**

5. Graph the data on a stem-and-leaf plot.

Stem	Leaf

6. Transfer the data to a vertical box-and-whisker plot.

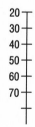

7. What are the extremes?

8. What is the interquartile range?

9. Why are the whiskers unequal?

10. How is an outlier determined? Are there any outlier values?

Study Guide

Integration: Statistics
Box-and-Whisker Plots

A box-and-whisker plot
displays the extremes,
the quartiles, and the
median for a set of data.
It may be drawn
horizontally or vertically.

Study the box at the
right. Note the dots
marking the extremes,
the quartiles, and the
median.

Data: 3, 7, 9, 14, 16, 19, 19, 25

Stem	Leaf
0	3 7 9
1	4 6 9 9
2	5

$1|6 = 16$
Interquartile range
is 19 − 8, or 11.

Box-and-Whisker Plot:

Lower extreme is 3.
Lower quartile is 8.
Median is 15.
Upper quartile is 19.
Upper extreme is 25.

Answer each question for the indicated box-and-whisker plot.

1. What are the upper and lower extremes?
   16; 4
2. What is the median? **12**

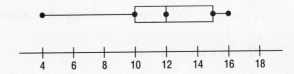

3. What are the upper and lower quartiles?
   15; 10
4. What is the interquartile range? **5**

Use the data given to complete the following.   **Data: 19, 49, 73, 30, 32, 46, 51, 30**

5. Graph the data on a stem-and-leaf
   plot.

Stem	Leaf
1	9
3	0 0 2
4	6 9
5	1
7	3

$4|6 = 46$

6. Transfer the data to a vertical box-
   and-whisker plot.

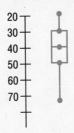

7. What are the extremes? **19; 73**

8. What is the interquartile range? **20**

9. Why are the whiskers unequal?
   **The difference between the
   LQ and the LV is less than the
   difference between the GV and
   the UQ.**

10. How is an outlier determined? Are
    there any outlier values?
    **Multiply 1.5 times the
    interquartile range, 20. Then
    add this product to the UQ, 50,
    and subtract it from the LQ, 30.
    There are no outliers.**

Graphing Inequalities in Two Variables

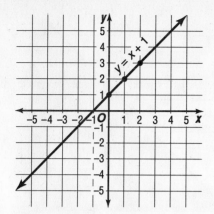

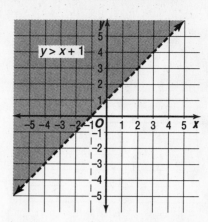

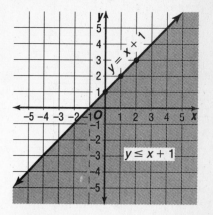

The graph of the equation $y = x + 1$ is a line that separates the coordinate plane into two regions. Each region is called a **half-plane.** The line for $y = x + 1$ is called the **boundary** for each half-plane.

The boundary line in both regions is the line for $y = x + 1$. In $y > x + 1$, the boundary is *not* part of the graph. The boundary is shown as a dashed line. All points above the line are part of the graph. This graph is called an **open half-plane.** In $y \leq x + 1$, the boundary *is* part of the graph and is shown as a solid line. The graph also contains all points below the line. This graph is called a **closed half-plane.**

Graph each inequality.

1. $y < 4$

2. $3x < y$

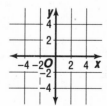

3. $2x - 3y \leq 6$

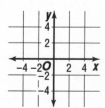

4. $-5x + 2 \geq y$

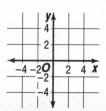

5. $x - y \geq 1$

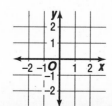

6. $-x > y$

Graphing Inequalities in Two Variables

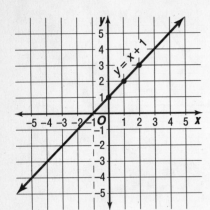
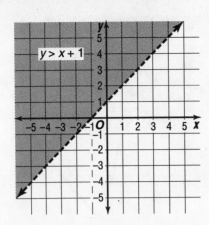
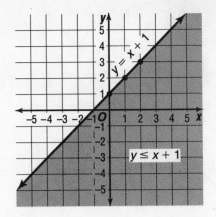

The graph of the equation $y = x + 1$ is a line that separates the coordinate plane into two regions. Each region is called a **half-plane.** The line for $y = x + 1$ is called the **boundary** for each half-plane.

The boundary line in both regions is the line for $y = x + 1$. In $y > x + 1$, the boundary is *not* part of the graph. The boundary is shown as a dashed line. All points above the line are part of the graph. This graph is called an **open half-plane.** In $y \leq x + 1$, the boundary *is* part of the graph and is shown as a solid line. The graph also contains all points below the line. This graph is called a **closed half-plane.**

Graph each inequality.

1. $y < 4$

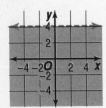

2. $3x < y$

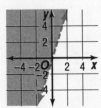

3. $2x - 3y \leq 6$

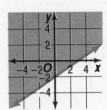

4. $-5x + 2 \geq y$

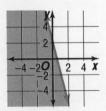

5. $x - y \geq 1$

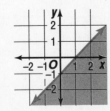

6. $-x > y$

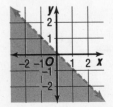

8-1

Study Guide

Graphing Systems of Equations

Two or more linear equations involving the same variables form a **system of equations.** The solution set for the system is the set of ordered pairs that satisfy both equations. One method for solving a system of equations is to graph the equations on the same coordinate plane.

Examples: Solve each system of equations by graphing.

$$x + y = 2$$
$$x - y = 4$$

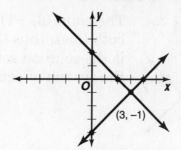

The point $(3, -1)$ lies on both lines, thus $(3, -1)$ is the solution set for the system of equations.

$$3x + y = 2$$
$$3x + y = 4$$
no solution

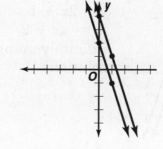

$$y = 2x + 1$$
$$2y = 4x + 2$$
infinitely many solutions

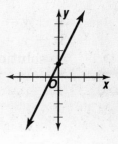

Use the graphs below to determine whether each system has one solution, no solution, or infinitely many solutions. If the system has one solution, name it.

1. $x - y = 1$
   $x + y = -1$

2. $x + 3y = 3$
   $2x + y = 2$

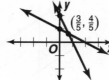

3. $2x + 3y = 6$
   $2x + 3y = -6$

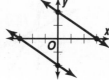

4. $x - y = 2$
   $2x - 2y = 4$

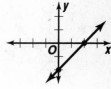

Graph each system of equations on a separate sheet of paper. Then determine whether the system has one solution, no solution, or infinitely many solutions. If the system has one solution, name it.

5. $4x - 2y = 4$
   $4x - 2y = 0$

6. $y = x + 2$
   $y = 2x - 1$

7. $x + y = 1$
   $3x + 3y = 3$

8. $2x - 2y = 2$
   $y = x$

Algebra 1

8-1

Study Guide

Graphing Systems of Equations

Two or more linear equations involving the same variables form a **system of equations.** The solution set for the system is the set of ordered pairs that satisfy both equations. One method for solving a system of equations is to graph the equations on the same coordinate plane.

Examples: Solve each system of equations by graphing.

$x + y = 2$
$x - y = 4$

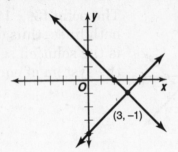

The point $(3, -1)$ lies on both lines, thus $(3, -1)$ is the solution set for the system of equations.

$3x + y = 2$
$3x + y = 4$
no solution

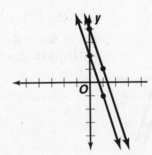

$y = 2x + 1$
$2y = 4x + 2$
infinitely many solutions

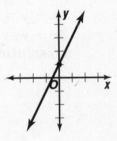

Use the graphs below to determine whether each system has one solution, <u>no</u> solution, or <u>infinitely many</u> solutions. If the system has one solution, name it.

1. $x - y = 1$
   $x + y = -1$

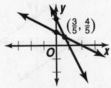

one solution
(0, −1)

2. $x + 3y = 3$
   $2x + y = 2$

one solution
$\left(\dfrac{3}{5}, \dfrac{4}{5}\right)$

3. $2x + 3y = 6$
   $2x + 3y = -6$

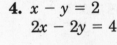

no solution

4. $x - y = 2$
   $2x - 2y = 4$

infinitely many solutions

Graph each system of equations on a separate sheet of paper. Then determine whether the system has <u>one</u> solution, <u>no</u> solution, or <u>infinitely many</u> solutions. If the system has one solution, name it.

5. $4x - 2y = 4$
   $4x - 2y = 0$
   no solution

6. $y = x + 2$
   $y = 2x - 1$
   one solution
   (3, 5)

7. $x + y = 1$
   $3x + 3y = 3$
   infinitely many solutions

8. $2x - 2y = 2$
   $y = x$
   no solution

Study Guide

Substitution

One method of solving systems of equations is by algebraic **substitution**.

Example: Solve $x + 3y = 7$ and $2x - 4y = -6$.

Solve the first equation for x.

$$x + 3y = 7$$
$$x = 7 - 3y$$

Substitute $7 - 3y$ for x in the second equation. Solve for y.

$$2(7 - 3y) - 4y = -6$$
$$14 - 6y - 4y = -6$$
$$-10y = -20$$
$$y = 2$$

Substitute 2 for y in either one of the two original equations to find the value of x.

$$x + 3(2) = 7$$
$$x + 6 = 7$$
$$x = 1$$

The solution of this system is $(1, 2)$.

Use substitution to solve each system of equations. If the system does not have exactly one solution, state whether it has no solution or infinitely many solutions.

1. $x = 3$
   $2y + x = 3$

2. $y = 2$
   $2x - 4y = 1$

3. $y = 3x - 7$
   $3x - y = 7$

4. $y = -x + 3$
   $2y + 2x = 4$

5. $x + y = 16$
   $2y = -2x + 2$

6. $x = 2y$
   $0.25x + 0.5y = 10$

Use a system of equations and substitution to solve each problem.

7. How much of a 10% saline solution should be mixed with a 20% saline solution to obtain 1000 milliliters of a 12% saline solution?

8. The tens digit of a two-digit number is 3 greater than the units digit. Eight times the sum of the digits is 1 less than the number. Find the number.

Algebra 1

Study Guide

Substitution

One method of solving systems of equations is by algebraic **substitution**.

Example: Solve $x + 3y = 7$ and $2x - 4y = -6$.

Solve the first equation for x.

$$x + 3y = 7$$
$$x = 7 - 3y$$

Substitute $7 - 3y$ for x in the second equation. Solve for y.

$$2(7 - 3y) - 4y = -6$$
$$14 - 6y - 4y = -6$$
$$-10y = -20$$
$$y = 2$$

Substitute 2 for y in either one of the two original equations to find the value of x.

$$x + 3(2) = 7$$
$$x + 6 = 7$$
$$x = 1$$

The solution of this system is $(1, 2)$.

Use substitution to solve each system of equations. If the system _does not_ have exactly one solution, state whether it has _no solution_ or _infinitely many_ solutions.

1. $x = 3$
   $2y + x = 3$
   (3, 0)

2. $y = 2$
   $2x - 4y = 1$
   $\left(\dfrac{9}{2}, 2\right)$

3. $y = 3x - 7$
   $3x - y = 7$
   infinitely many

4. $y = -x + 3$
   $2y + 2x = 4$
   no solution

5. $x + y = 16$
   $2y = -2x + 2$
   no solution

6. $x = 2y$
   $0.25x + 0.5y = 10$
   (20, 10)

Use a system of equations and substitution to solve each problem.

7. How much of a 10% saline solution should be mixed with a 20% saline solution to obtain 1000 milliliters of a 12% saline solution?
   800 mL of 10% solution and 200 mL of 20% solution

8. The tens digit of a two-digit number is 3 greater than the units digit. Eight times the sum of the digits is 1 less than the number. Find the number.
   41

Study Guide

Elimination Using Addition and Subtraction

In systems of equations where the coefficient of the x or y terms are additive inverses, solve the system by adding the equations. Because one of the variables is eliminated, this method is called **elimination.**

Example: Use elimination to solve the system of equations
$x - 3y = 7$ and $3x + 3y = 9$.

Add the two equations.

$$x - 3y = 7$$
$$3x + 3y = 9$$
$$4x = 16$$
$$x = 4$$

Substitute 4 for x in either original equation and solve for y.

$$4 - 3y = 7$$
$$-3y = 7 - 4$$
$$-3y = 3$$
$$y = -1$$

The solution of the system is $(4, -1)$.

Use elimination to solve each system of equations.

1. $2x + 2y = -2$
$3x - 2y = 12$

2. $4x - 2y = -1$
$-4x + 4y = -2$

3. $x - y = 2$
$x + y = -3$

4. $6x + 5y = 4$
$6x - 7y = -20$

5. $2x - 3y = 12$
$4x + 3y = 24$

6. $0.1x + 0.3y = 0.9$
$0.1x = 0.3y + 0.2$

Use a system of equations and elimination to solve each problem.

7. Two angles are supplementary. The measure of one angle is 10 more than three times the other. Find the measure of each angle.

8. Rema is older than Ken. The difference of their ages is 12 and the sum of their ages is 50. Find the age of each.

9. The sum of two numbers is 70 and their difference is 24. Find the two numbers.

10. The sum of the digits of a two-digit number is 12. The difference of the digits is 2. Find the number if the units digit is larger than the tens digit.

NAME_____ DATE _____

Study Guide

Elimination Using Addition and Subtraction

In systems of equations where the coefficient of the x or y terms are additive inverses, solve the system by adding the equations. Because one of the variables is eliminated, this method is called **elimination.**

Example: Use elimination to solve the system of equations
$x - 3y = 7$ and $3x + 3y = 9$.

Add the two equations.

$$x - 3y = 7$$
$$\underline{3x + 3y = 9}$$
$$4x = 16$$
$$x = 4$$

Substitute 4 for x in either original equation and solve for y.

$$4 - 3y = 7$$
$$-3y = 7 - 4$$
$$-3y = 3$$
$$y = -1$$

The solution of the system is $(4, -1)$.

Use elimination to solve each system of equations.

1. $2x + 2y = -2$
$3x - 2y = 12$
(2, −3)

2. $4x - 2y = -1$
$-4x + 4y = -2$
$\left(-1, -\dfrac{3}{2}\right)$

3. $x - y = 2$
$x + y = -3$
$\left(-\dfrac{1}{2}, -\dfrac{5}{2}\right)$

4. $6x + 5y = 4$
$6x - 7y = -20$
(−1, 2)

5. $2x - 3y = 12$
$4x + 3y = 24$
(6, 0)

6. $0.1x + 0.3y = 0.9$
$0.1x = 0.3y + 0.2$
$\left(\dfrac{11}{2}, \dfrac{7}{6}\right)$

Use a system of equations and elimination to solve each problem.

7. Two angles are supplementary. The measure of one angle is 10 more than three times the other. Find the measure of each angle.
42.5°, 137.5°

8. Rema is older than Ken. The difference of their ages is 12 and the sum of their ages is 50. Find the age of each.
Rema is 31 and Ken is 19

9. The sum of two numbers is 70 and their difference is 24. Find the two numbers. **23 and 47**

10. The sum of the digits of a two-digit number is 12. The difference of the digits is 2. Find the number if the units digit is larger than the tens digit. **57**

 Algebra 1

Study Guide

Elimination Using Multiplication

Some systems of equations cannot be solved simply by adding or subtracting the equations. One or both equations must first be multiplied by a number before the system can be solved by elimination. Consider the following example.

Example: Use elimination to solve the system of equations
$x + 10y = 3$ and $4x + 5y = 5$.

$x + 10y = 3$ Multiply $x + 10y = 3$ $-4x - 40y = -12$
$4x + 5y = 5$ by -4. $\underline{4x + 5y = 5}$
              Then add the $-35y = -7$
              equations. $y = \dfrac{1}{5}$

Substitute $\dfrac{1}{5}$ for y into either original equation and solve for x.

$$x + 10\left(\dfrac{1}{5}\right) = 3$$
$$x + 2 = 3$$
$$x = 1$$

The solution of the system is $\left(1, \dfrac{1}{5}\right)$.

Use elimination to solve each system of equations.

1. $3x + 2y = 0$
    $x - 5y = 17$

2. $2x + 3y = 6$
    $x + 2y = 5$

3. $3x - y = 2$
    $x + 2y = 3$

4. $4x + 5y = 6$
    $6x - 7y = -20$

Use a system of equations and elimination to solve each problem.

5. The length of Sally's garden is 4 meters greater than 3 times the width. The perimeter of her garden is 72 meters. What are the dimensions of Sally's garden?

6. Anita is $4\dfrac{1}{2}$ years older than Basilio. Three times Anita's age added to six times Basilio's age is 36. How old are Anita and Basilio?

Study Guide

Elimination Using Multiplication

Some systems of equations cannot be solved simply by adding or subtracting the equations. One or both equations must first be multiplied by a number before the system can be solved by elimination. Consider the following example.

Example: Use elimination to solve the system of equations
$x + 10y = 3$ and $4x + 5y = 5$.

$x + 10y = 3$ Multiply $x + 10y = 3$ $-4x - 40y = -12$
$4x + 5y = 5$ by -4. $\underline{4x + 5y = 5}$
     Then add the $-35y = -7$
     equations. $y = \dfrac{1}{5}$

Substitute $\dfrac{1}{5}$ for y into either original equation and solve for x.

$$x + 10\left(\dfrac{1}{5}\right) = 3$$
$$x + 2 = 3$$
$$x = 1$$

The solution of the system is $\left(1, \dfrac{1}{5}\right)$.

Use elimination to solve each system of equations.

1. $3x + 2y = 0$
    $x - 5y = 17$
(2, −3)

2. $2x + 3y = 6$
    $x + 2y = 5$
(−3, 4)

3. $3x - y = 2$
    $x + 2y = 3$
(1, 1)

4. $4x + 5y = 6$
    $6x - 7y = -20$
(−1, 2)

Use a system of equations and elimination to solve each problem.

5. The length of Sally's garden is 4 meters greater than 3 times the width. The perimeter of her garden is 72 meters. What are the dimensions of Sally's garden?
28 meters by 8 meters

6. Anita is $4\dfrac{1}{2}$ years older than Basilio. Three times Anita's age added to six times Basilio's age is 36. How old are Anita and Basilio?
Basilio is $2\dfrac{1}{2}$ yr and Anita is 7 yr.

Study Guide

Graphing Systems of Inequalities

The solution of a system of inequalities is the set of all ordered pairs that satisfy both inequalities. To find the solution of the system

$$y > x + 2$$
$$y \leq -2x - 1,$$

graph each inequality. The graph of each inequality is called a **half-plane.** The intersection of the half-planes represents the solution of the system. The graphs of $y = x + 2$ and $y = -2x - 1$ are the boundaries of the region.

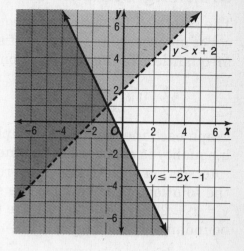

An inequality containing an absolute value expression can be graphed by graphing an equivalent system of two inequalities.

Solve each system of inequalities by graphing.

1. $y \geq 2x$
   $y \geq -1$

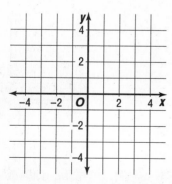

2. $5x - 2y < 6$
   $y > -x + 1$

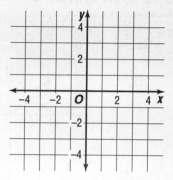

3. $|y| > x$

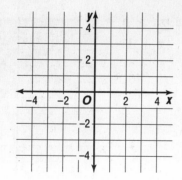

4. $-x + y \leq 6$
   $x + y \leq 2$

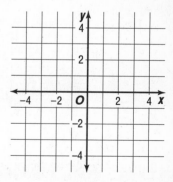

5. Write a system of inequalities for the graph at the right.

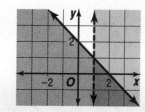

8-5

Study Guide

Graphing Systems of Inequalities

The solution of a system of inequalities is the set of all ordered pairs that satisfy both inequalities. To find the solution of the system

$$y > x + 2$$
$$y \leq -2x - 1,$$

graph each inequality. The graph of each inequality is called a **half-plane.** The intersection of the half-planes represents the solution of the system. The graphs of $y = x + 2$ and $y = -2x - 1$ are the boundaries of the region.

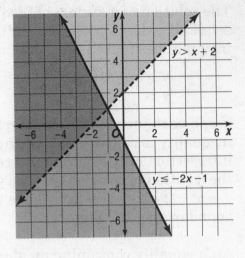

An inequality containing an absolute value expression can be graphed by graphing an equivalent system of two inequalities.

Solve each system of inequalities by graphing.

1. $y \geq 2x$
   $y \geq -1$

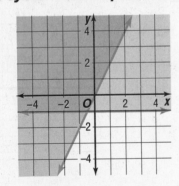

2. $5x - 2y < 6$
   $y > -x + 1$

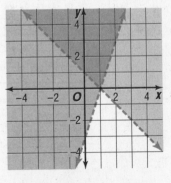

3. $|y| > x$

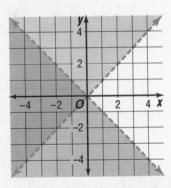

4. $-x + y \leq 6$
   $x + y \leq 2$

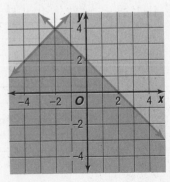

5. Write a system of inequalities for the graph at the right.
   $x + y \leq 2$
   $x > 1$

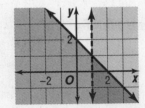

Study Guide

Multiplying Monomials

When you multiply monomials, you use the following rules for all numbers a and b and any integers m, n, and p.

	Rule	Example
Product of Powers	For any number a, and all integers m and n, $a^m \cdot a^n = a^{m+n}$.	$a^2 \cdot a^6 = a^{2+6}$ $= a^8$
Power of a Power	For any number a, and all integers m and n, $(a^m)^n = a^{mn}$.	$(x^2)^6 = x^{2 \cdot 6}$ $= x^{12}$
Power of a Product	For all numbers a and b, and any integer m, $(ab)^m = a^m b^m$.	$(pq)^4 = p^4 q^4$
Power of a Monomial	For all numbers a and b, and all integers m, n, and p, $(a^m b^n)^p = a^{mp} b^{np}$.	$(s^4 t)^3 = (s^4 t^1)^3$ $= s^{4 \cdot 3} t^{1 \cdot 3}$ $= s^{12} t^3$

Simplify.

1. $[n^5(n^2)]$

2. $b(b^4)$

3. $(-7x^2)(x^4)$

4. $(2a^2)(8a)$

5. $(rs)(rs^3)(s^2)$

6. $(x^2 y)(4xy^3)$

7. $\frac{1}{3}(2a^3 b)(6b^3)$

8. $(-5nx)(4x^2)(n^4)$

9. $(n^3)^5$

10. $(a^4)^6$

11. $-3(ab^4)^3$

12. $(-3ab^4)^3$

13. $(4x^2 b)^3$

14. $(4x)^2(b^3)$

15. $(-2m^5 n^6)^2$

16. $-2m^5(n^6)^2$

17. $2(3x)^3$

18. $-3(2x)^5$

19. $(-2n^6 y^5)(-6n^3 y^2)(ny)^3$

20. $(-3a^3 n^4)(-3a^3 n)^4$

Study Guide

Multiplying Monomials

When you multiply monomials, you use the following rules for all numbers a and b and any integers m, n, and p.

	Rule	Example
Product of Powers	For any number a, and all integers m and n, $a^m \cdot a^n = a^{m+n}$.	$a^2 \cdot a^6 = a^{2+6}$ $= a^8$
Power of a Power	For any number a, and all integers m and n, $(a^m)^n = a^{mn}$.	$(x^2)^6 = x^{2 \cdot 6}$ $= x^{12}$
Power of a Product	For all numbers a and b, and any integer m, $(ab)^m = a^m b^m$.	$(pq)^4 = p^4 q^4$
Power of a Monomial	For all numbers a and b, and all integers m, n, and p, $(a^m b^n)^p = a^{mp} b^{np}$.	$(s^4 t)^3 = (s^4 t^1)^3$ $= s^{4 \cdot 3} t^{1 \cdot 3}$ $= s^{12} t^3$

Simplify.

1. $[n^5(n^2)]$ n^7

2. $b(b^4)$ b^5

3. $(-7x^2)(x^4)$ $-7x^6$

4. $(2a^2)(8a)$ $16a^3$

5. $(rs)(rs^3)(s^2)$ $r^2 s^6$

6. $(x^2 y)(4xy^3)$ $4x^3 y^4$

7. $\frac{1}{3}(2a^3 b)(6b^3)$ $4a^3 b^4$

8. $(-5nx)(4x^2)(n^4)$ $-20n^5 x^3$

9. $(n^3)^5$ n^{15}

10. $(a^4)^6$ a^{24}

11. $-3(ab^4)^3$ $-3a^3 b^{12}$

12. $(-3ab^4)^3$ $-27a^3 b^{12}$

13. $(4x^2 b)^3$ $64x^6 b^3$

14. $(4x)^2(b^3)$ $16x^2 b^3$

15. $(-2m^5 n^6)^2$ $4m^{10} n^{12}$

16. $-2m^5(n^6)^2$ $-2m^5 n^{12}$

17. $2(3x)^3$ $54x^3$

18. $-3(2x)^5$ $-96x^5$

19. $(-2n^6 y^5)(-6n^3 y^2)(ny)^3$ $12n^{12} y^{10}$

20. $(-3a^3 n^4)(-3a^3 n)^4$ $-243a^{15} n^8$

Algebra 1

NAME_____ DATE _____

Study Guide

Student Edition
Pages 501–505

Dividing by Monomials

Study the following exponent rules.

	Rule	Example
Quotient of Powers	For all integers m and n, and any nonzero number a, $\dfrac{a^m}{a^n} = a^{m-n}$.	$q^9 \div q^4 = q^{9-4}$ $= q^5$
Zero Exponent	For any nonzero number a, $a^0 = 1$.	$4^0 = 1$ $6^0 = 1$
Negative Exponents	For any nonzero number a and any integer n, $a^{-n} = \dfrac{1}{a^n}$.	$\dfrac{r^3}{r^6} = \dfrac{r \cdot r \cdot r}{r \cdot r \cdot r \cdot r \cdot r \cdot r}$ $= \dfrac{1}{r^3}$ or $\dfrac{r^3}{r^6} = r^{3-6} = r^{-3}$

Simplify. Assume no denominator is equal to zero.

1. $\dfrac{a^2}{a}$

2. $\dfrac{x^5 y^3}{x^5 y^2}$

3. $\dfrac{15a^3}{45a^2}$

4. $\dfrac{s^{-3} t^{-5}}{(s^2 t^3)^{-1}}$

5. $\dfrac{a^5 b^3}{a^2 b^2}$

6. $\dfrac{k^0}{k^7}$

7. $\dfrac{(6a^{-1}b)^2}{(b^2)^4}$

8. $\dfrac{66 w^3 x^6 y^9}{-22 wxy^7}$

9. $\left(\dfrac{4m^2 n^2}{8m^{-1}l}\right)^0$

10. $\dfrac{15x^3}{5x^0}$

11. $\dfrac{x^2}{x^3}$

12. $\dfrac{(3st)^2 u^{-4}}{s^{-1} t^2 u^7}$

13. $\dfrac{b^5}{b^6}$

14. $\dfrac{x^9}{x^2}$

15. $\dfrac{24 w^7 t^4}{6 w^3 t^2}$

16. $\dfrac{9x^2 z^5}{-3xz^3}$

17. $\dfrac{(-x^{-1}y)^0}{4w^{-1}y^2}$

18. $\dfrac{wt^3 x}{wx}$

19. $\dfrac{w^2}{w}$

20. $\dfrac{(a^2 b^3)^2}{(ab)^{-2}}$

Algebra 1

NAME_____ DATE _____

Study Guide

Dividing by Monomials

Study the following exponent rules.

	Rule	Example
Quotient of Powers	For all integers m and n, and any nonzero number a, $\frac{a^m}{a^n} = a^{m-n}$.	$q^9 \div q^4 = q^{9-4}$ $= q^5$
Zero Exponent	For any nonzero number a, $a^0 = 1$.	$4^0 = 1$ $6^0 = 1$
Negative Exponents	For any nonzero number a and any integer n, $a^{-n} = \frac{1}{a^n}$.	$\frac{r^3}{r^6} = \frac{r \cdot r \cdot r}{r \cdot r \cdot r \cdot r \cdot r \cdot r}$ $= \frac{1}{r^3}$ or $\frac{r^3}{r^6} = r^{3-6} = r^{-3}$

Simplify. Assume no denominator is equal to zero.

1. $\frac{a^2}{a}$ **a**

2. $\frac{x^5y^3}{x^5y^2}$ **y**

3. $\frac{15a^3}{45a^2}$ **$\frac{a}{3}$**

4. $\frac{s^{-3}t^{-5}}{(s^2t^3)^{-1}}$ **$\frac{1}{st^2}$**

5. $\frac{a^5b^3}{a^2b^2}$ **a^3b**

6. $\frac{k^0}{k^7}$ **$\frac{1}{k^7}$**

7. $\frac{(6a^{-1}b)^2}{(b^2)^4}$ **$\frac{36}{a^2b^6}$**

8. $\frac{66w^3x^6y^9}{-22wxy^7}$ **$-3w^2x^5y^2$**

9. $\left(\frac{4m^2n^2}{8m^{-1}l}\right)^0$ **1**

10. $\frac{15x^3}{5x^0}$ **$3x^3$**

11. $\frac{x^2}{x^3}$ **$\frac{1}{x}$**

12. $\frac{(3st)^2u^{-4}}{s^{-1}t^2u^7}$ **$\frac{9s^3}{u^{11}}$**

13. $\frac{b^5}{b^6}$ **$\frac{1}{b}$**

14. $\frac{x^9}{x^2}$ **x^7**

15. $\frac{24w^7t^4}{6w^3t^2}$ **$4w^4t^2$**

16. $\frac{9x^2z^5}{-3xz^3}$ **$-3xz^2$**

17. $\frac{(-x^{-1}y)^0}{4w^{-1}y^2}$ **$\frac{w}{4y^2}$**

18. $\frac{wt^3x}{wx}$ **t^3**

19. $\frac{w^2}{w}$ **w**

20. $\frac{(a^2b^3)^2}{(ab)^{-2}}$ **a^6b^8**

Algebra 1

Scientific Notation

Scientists use scientific notation to express very large or very small numbers. A number is expressed in scientific notation when it is expressed as the product of a number between one and ten, and a power of ten.

Example 1: $37,000 = 3.7 \times 10^4$ **Example 2:** $0.00391 = 3.91 \times 10^{-3}$

You can find products or quotients of numbers that are expressed in scientific notation by following the rules for multiplying and dividing monomials and powers.

Example 3: $\dfrac{8.4 \times 10^8}{4.2 \times 10^5} = \dfrac{8.4}{4.2} \times \dfrac{10^8}{10^5}$
$= 2 \times 10^3$, or 2000

Example 4: $(6700)(0.00002)$
$= (6.7 \times 10^3)(2 \times 10^{-5})$
$= (6.7 \times 2)(10^3 \times 10^{-5})$
$= 13.4 \times 10^{-2}$
$= 1.34 \times 10^{-1}$, or 0.134

Express each number in scientific notation.

1. 0.0000456 2. 0.01 3. $590,000,000$ 4. 640×10^5

Evaluate. Express each result in scientific and standard notation.

5. $\dfrac{1.4 \times 10^4}{0.2 \times 10^2}$ 6. $\dfrac{3.3 \times 10^{-12}}{1.1 \times 10^{-14}}$ 7. $\dfrac{0.000042}{600}$

8. $(2 \times 10^4)(4 \times 10^{-5})$ 9. $(77 \times 10^4)(0.02 \times 10^3)$ 10. $(3.2 \times 10^{-2})(2.0 \times 10^2)$

11. $250,000 \div 0.0005$ 12. $(0.00004)(20,000)$ 13. $(1.5 \times 10^5)(3.3 \times 10^{-4})$

         Algebra 1

Study Guide

Scientific Notation

Scientists use scientific notation to express very large or very small numbers. A number is expressed in scientific notation when it is expressed as the product of a number between one and ten, and a power of ten.

Example 1: $37{,}000 = 3.7 \times 10^4$ **Example 2:** $0.00391 = 3.91 \times 10^{-3}$

You can find products or quotients of numbers that are expressed in scientific notation by following the rules for multiplying and dividing monomials and powers.

Example 3: $\dfrac{8.4 \times 10^8}{4.2 \times 10^5} = \dfrac{8.4}{4.2} \times \dfrac{10^8}{10^5}$
$= 2 \times 10^3$, or 2000

Example 4: $(6700)(0.00002)$
$= (6.7 \times 10^3)(2 \times 10^{-5})$
$= (6.7 \times 2)(10^3 \times 10^{-5})$
$= 13.4 \times 10^{-2}$
$= 1.34 \times 10^{-1}$, or 0.134

Express each number in scientific notation.

1. 0.0000456
   4.56×10^{-5}

2. 0.01
   10^{-2}

3. $590{,}000{,}000$
   5.9×10^8

4. 640×10^5
   6.4×10^7

Evaluate. Express each result in scientific and standard notation.

5. $\dfrac{1.4 \times 10^4}{0.2 \times 10^2}$
   7×10^2; 700

6. $\dfrac{3.3 \times 10^{-12}}{1.1 \times 10^{-14}}$
   3×10^2; 300

7. $\dfrac{0.000042}{600}$
   7×10^{-8};
   0.00000007

8. $(2 \times 10^4)(4 \times 10^{-5})$
   8×10^{-1}; 0.8

9. $(77 \times 10^4)(0.02 \times 10^3)$
   1.54×10^7;
   $15{,}400{,}000$

10. $(3.2 \times 10^{-2})(2.0 \times 10^2)$
    6.4×10^0; 6.4

11. $250{,}000 \div 0.0005$
    5×10^8;
    $500{,}000{,}000$

12. $(0.00004)(20{,}000)$
    8×10^{-1}; 0.8

13. $(1.5 \times 10^5)(3.3 \times 10^{-4})$
    4.95×10^1; 49.5

Study Guide

Polynomials

A **polynomial** is a monomial or a sum of monomials. A **binomial** is the sum of two monomials, and a **trinomial** is the sum of three monomials.

Examples of each type of polynomial are given in the following chart.

Monomial	Binomial	Trinomial
$5x^2$	$3x + 2$	$5x^2 - 2x + 7$
$4abc$	$4x + 5y$	$a^2 + 2ab + b^2$

The **degree** of a monomial is the sum of the exponents of its variables.

Monomial	Degree
$5x^2$	2
$4ab^3c^4$	$1 + 3 + 4 = 8$

To find the degree of a polynomial, first find the degree of each of its terms. The degree of the polynomial is the greatest of the degrees of its terms. The terms of a polynomial are usually arranged so that the powers of one variable are in either ascending or descending order.

Ascending Order: $3 + 5a - 8a^2 + a^3$
Descending Order: (in x) $x^5y^2 - x^4 + x^3y^2 + 5xy$

Find the degree of each polynomial.

1. $4x^2y^3z$

2. $-2abc$

3. $15m$

4. $s + 5t$

5. 22

6. $18x^2y + 4yz - 10y$

7. $x^4 - 6x^2 - 2x^3 - 10$

8. $2x^3y^2 - 4xy^3$

9. $-2r^8s^4 + 7r^2s - 4r^7s^6$

Arrange the terms of each polynomial so that the powers of x are in descending order.

10. $24x^2y - 12x^3y^2 + 6x^4$

11. $20x - 10x^2 + 5x^3$

12. $9bx + 3bx^2 - 6x^3$

13. $-15x^3 + 10x^4y^2 + 7xy^2$

14. $ax^2 + 8a^2x^5 - 4$

15. $x^5 + x^2 - x^3$

Arrange the terms of each polynomial so that the powers of x are in ascending order.

16. $x^4 + x^3 + x^2$

17. $2x^3 - x + 3x^7$

18. $-5cx + 10c^2x^3 + 15cx^2$

19. $3 + 9x^4 + 9x^3$

20. $-4nx - 5n^3x^3 + 5$

21. $4xy + 2y + 5x^2$

NAME_____ DATE _____

Study Guide

Polynomials

A **polynomial** is a monomial or a sum of monomials. A **binomial** is the sum of two monomials, and a **trinomial** is the sum of three monomials.

Examples of each type of polynomial are given in the following chart.

Monomial	Binomial	Trinomial
$5x^2$	$3x + 2$	$5x^2 - 2x + 7$
$4abc$	$4x + 5y$	$a^2 + 2ab + b^2$

The **degree** of a monomial is the sum of the exponents of its variables.

Monomial	Degree
$5x^2$	2
$4ab^3c^4$	$1 + 3 + 4 = 8$

To find the degree of a polynomial, first find the degree of each of its terms. The degree of the polynomial is the greatest of the degrees of its terms. The terms of a polynomial are usually arranged so that the powers of one variable are in either ascending or descending order.

Ascending Order: $3 + 5a - 8a^2 + a^3$
Descending Order: (in x) $x^5y^2 - x^4 + x^3y^2 + 5xy$

Find the degree of each polynomial.

1. $4x^2y^3z$ **6**

2. $-2abc$ **3**

3. $15m$ **1**

4. $s + 5t$ **1**

5. 22 **0**

6. $18x^2y + 4yz - 10y$ **3**

7. $x^4 - 6x^2 - 2x^3 - 10$ **4**

8. $2x^3y^2 - 4xy^3$ **5**

9. $-2r^8s^4 + 7r^2s - 4r^7s^6$ **13**

Arrange the terms of each polynomial so that the powers of x are in descending order.

10. $24x^2y - 12x^3y^2 + 6x^4$
$6x^4 - 12x^3y^2 + 24x^2y$

11. $20x - 10x^2 + 5x^3$
$5x^3 - 10x^2 + 20x$

12. $9bx + 3bx^2 - 6x^3$
$-6x^3 + 3bx^2 + 9bx$

13. $-15x^3 + 10x^4y^2 + 7xy^2$
$10x^4y^2 - 15x^3 + 7xy^2$

14. $ax^2 + 8a^2x^5 - 4$
$8a^2x^5 + ax^2 - 4$

15. $x^5 + x^2 - x^3$
$x^5 - x^3 + x^2$

Arrange the terms of each polynomial so that the powers of x are in ascending order.

16. $x^4 + x^3 + x^2$
$x^2 + x^3 + x^4$

17. $2x^3 - x + 3x^7$
$-x + 2x^3 + 3x^7$

18. $-5cx + 10c^2x^3 + 15cx^2$
$-5cx + 15cx^2 + 10c^2x^3$

19. $3 + 9x^4 + 9x^3$
$3 + 9x^3 + 9x^4$

20. $-4nx - 5n^3x^3 + 5$
$5 - 4nx - 5n^3x^3$

21. $4xy + 2y + 5x^2$
$2y + 4xy + 5x^2$

Algebra 1

Study Guide

Adding and Subtracting Polynomials

You can use the following methods when you add polynomials.

Example 1: Find $(4x + 6y) + (3x + 9y)$.

$$(4x + 6y) + (3x + 9y) = (4x + 3x) + (6y + 9y)$$
$$= (4 + 3)x + (6 + 9)y$$
$$= 7x + 15y$$

Example 2: Find $(3x^2 - 5xy + 8y^2) + (2x^2 + xy - 6y^2)$.

$$
\begin{array}{r}
3x^2 - 5xy + 8y^2 \\
2x^2 + \ xy - 6y^2 \\
\hline
5x^2 - 4xy + 2y^2
\end{array}
$$

You can subtract a polynomial by adding its additive inverse.

Subtraction

— additive inverses —

Addition

$$-1 - (-4) = 3 \qquad -1 + 4 = 3$$

Example 3: Find $(7x^2 - 8) - (-3x^2 + 1)$.

Method 1

$$(7x^2 - 8) - (-3x^2 + 1)$$
$$= 7x^2 - 8 + 3x^2 - 1$$
$$= (7x^2 + 3x^2) + (-8 - 1)$$
$$= 10x^2 - 9$$

Method 2

$$
\begin{array}{r}
7x^2 - 8 \\
(-) \quad -3x^2 + 1 \\
\hline
\end{array}
\qquad
\begin{array}{r}
7x^2 - 8 \\
(+) \quad 3x^2 - 1 \\
\hline
10x^2 - 9
\end{array}
$$

Find each sum or difference.

1. $(4a - 5) + (3a + 6)$

2. $(3x^2 - 5xy^2 + y^3) + (-3x^2 + 5xy^2 - y^3)$

3. $(3p^2 - 2p + 3) + (p^2 - 7p + 7)$

4. $(x^2 + y^2) - (-x^2 + y^2)$

5. $(2x^2 + 5xy + 4y^2) - (2x^2 + 5xy + 4y^2)$

6. $(2a^2 - ab + b^2) + (3a^2 + 5ab - 7ab^2)$

7.
$$
\begin{array}{r}
6x^2 + 3x \\
(+) \quad x^2 - 4x - 3 \\
\hline
\end{array}
$$

8.
$$
\begin{array}{r}
5x + 1\frac{1}{2}y + \frac{1}{4} \\
(+) \quad 2x \qquad\quad - 7 \\
\hline
\end{array}
$$

9.
$$
\begin{array}{r}
x^2 + 2xy + y^2 \\
x^2 - \ xy - y^2 \\
(+) \quad 3x^2 - 2xy - y^2 \\
\hline
\end{array}
$$

10.
$$
\begin{array}{r}
10x^2 + 5x - 6 \\
(-) \quad 8x^2 - 2x + 7 \\
\hline
\end{array}
$$

11.
$$
\begin{array}{r}
4.2x^2 \qquad\quad - 3.2 \\
(-) \quad 5.9x^2 + 2.6x - 1.9 \\
\hline
\end{array}
$$

12.
$$
\begin{array}{r}
7p^2q^2 - 8pq + 9 \\
(-) \quad p^2q^2 - 9pq - 10 \\
\hline
\end{array}
$$

NAME_____ DATE _____

Study Guide

Adding and Subtracting Polynomials

You can use the following methods when you add polynomials.

Example 1: Find $(4x + 6y) + (3x + 9y)$.

$$(4x + 6y) + (3x + 9y) = (4x + 3x) + (6y + 9y)$$
$$= (4 + 3)x + (6 + 9)y$$
$$= 7x + 15y$$

Example 2: Find $(3x^2 - 5xy + 8y^2) + (2x^2 + xy - 6y^2)$.

$$3x^2 - 5xy + 8y^2$$
$$\underline{2x^2 + \ xy - 6y^2}$$
$$5x^2 - 4xy + 2y^2$$

You can subtract a polynomial by adding its additive inverse.

Subtraction ←——— additive inverses ———→ **Addition**

$$-1 - (-4) = 3 \qquad\qquad -1 + 4 = 3$$

Example 3: Find $(7x^2 - 8) - (-3x^2 + 1)$.

Method 1

$(7x^2 - 8) - (-3x^2 + 1)$

$= 7x^2 - 8 + 3x^2 - 1$

$= (7x^2 + 3x^2) + (-8 - 1)$

$= 10x^2 - 9$

Method 2

$$\begin{array}{r} 7x^2 - 8 \\ (-) \ -3x^2 + 1 \\ \hline \end{array} \qquad \begin{array}{r} 7x^2 - 8 \\ (+) \ 3x^2 - 1 \\ \hline 10x^2 - 9 \end{array}$$

Find each sum or difference.

1. $(4a - 5) + (3a + 6)$ **$7a + 1$**

2. $(3x^2 - 5xy^2 + y^3) + (-3x^2 + 5xy^2 - y^3)$
0

3. $(3p^2 - 2p + 3) + (p^2 - 7p + 7)$
$4p^2 - 9p + 10$

4. $(x^2 + y^2) - (-x^2 + y^2)$
$2x^2$

5. $(2x^2 + 5xy + 4y^2) - (2x^2 + 5xy + 4y^2)$
0

6. $(2a^2 - ab + b^2) + (3a^2 + 5ab - 7ab^2)$
$5a^2 + 4ab - 7ab^2 + b^2$

7. $\begin{array}{r} 6x^2 + 3x \\ (+) \ \ x^2 - 4x - 3 \\ \hline \mathbf{7x^2 - x - 3} \end{array}$

8. $\begin{array}{r} 5x + 1\frac{1}{2}y + \frac{1}{4} \\ (+) \ 2x \qquad\quad - 7 \\ \hline \mathbf{7x + 1\frac{1}{2}y - 6\frac{3}{4}} \end{array}$

9. $\begin{array}{r} x^2 + 2xy + y^2 \\ x^2 - \ xy - y^2 \\ (+) \ 3x^2 - 2xy - y^2 \\ \hline \mathbf{5x^2 - xy - y^2} \end{array}$

10. $\begin{array}{r} 10x^2 + 5x - 6 \\ (-) \ \ 8x^2 - 2x + 7 \\ \hline \mathbf{2x^2 + 7x - 13} \end{array}$

11. $\begin{array}{r} 4.2x^2 \qquad\quad - 3.2 \\ (-) \ 5.9x^2 + 2.6x - 1.9 \\ \hline \mathbf{-1.7x^2 - 2.6x - 1.3} \end{array}$

12. $\begin{array}{r} 7p^2q^2 - 8pq + \ 9 \\ (-) \ \ p^2q^2 - 9pq - 10 \\ \hline \mathbf{6p^2q^2 + pq + 19} \end{array}$

NAME_____ DATE _____

Study Guide

Multiplying a Polynomial by a Monomial

The example below shows how the distributive property can be used to multiply a polynomial by a monomial.

Example 1: $6a(2a^2 + 5) = 6a(2a^2) + 6a(5)$
$$= 12a^3 + 30a$$

Many equations contain polynomials that must be added, subtracted, or multiplied before the equation can be solved.

Example 2:
Solve $-5 - (10 - 3p) = 12$.
$$-5 - (10 - 3p) = 12$$
$$-5 - 10 + 3p = 12$$
$$-15 + 3p = 12$$
$$-15 + 15 + 3p = 12 + 15$$
$$3p = 27$$
$$\frac{3p}{3} = \frac{27}{3}$$
$$p = 9$$

Example 3:
Solve $4(n - 2) + 5n = 6(3 - n) + 18$.
$$4(n - 2) + 5n = 6(3 - n) + 18$$
$$4n - 8 + 5n = 18 - 6n + 18$$
$$9n - 8 = 36 - 6n$$
$$9n + 6n - 8 + 8 = 36 + 8 - 6n + 6n$$
$$15n = 44$$
$$\frac{15n}{15} = \frac{44}{15}$$
$$n = 2\frac{14}{15}$$

Find each product.

1. $5(2a + 3b)$

2. $3x(4x - 2y)$

3. $-4(a^2 - b^2)$

4. $8b\left(b^2 - \frac{1}{2}b\right)$

5. $-5t^2\left(\frac{1}{25}t^2 - \frac{1}{25}t + \frac{1}{5}\right)$

6. $\left(\frac{1}{2}x + y\right)\left(\frac{1}{2}y\right)$

Simplify.

7. $4r(2r^2 - 3r + 5) + 6r(4r^2 + 2r + 8)$

8. $2b(b^2 + 4b + 8) - 3b(3b^2 + 9b - 18)$

Solve each equation.

9. $3(x + 5) - 6 = 18$

10. $3x(x - 5) - 3x^2 = -30$

11. $(4y - 3) - 8y + 6 = 19$

12. Ria's corn field has a perimeter of 18,000 meters. The length of one side is 3 meters less than twice the width. What are the dimensions of the field?

13. Three sides of a triangle have measures that are consecutive even integers. What are the lengths of the sides if the perimeter is 114 meters?

Multiplying a Polynomial by a Monomial

The example below shows how the distributive property can be used to multiply a polynomial by a monomial.

Example 1: $6a(2a^2 + 5) = 6a(2a^2) + 6a(5)$
$$= 12a^3 + 30a$$

Many equations contain polynomials that must be added, subtracted, or multiplied before the equation can be solved.

Example 2:
Solve $-5 - (10 - 3p) = 12$.
$-5 - (10 - 3p) = 12$
$-5 - 10 + 3p = 12$
$-15 + 3p = 12$
$-15 + 15 + 3p = 12 + 15$
$3p = 27$
$\dfrac{3p}{3} = \dfrac{27}{3}$
$p = 9$

Example 3:
Solve $4(n - 2) + 5n = 6(3 - n) + 18$.
$4(n - 2) + 5n = 6(3 - n) + 18$
$4n - 8 + 5n = 18 - 6n + 18$
$9n - 8 = 36 - 6n$
$9n + 6n - 8 + 8 = 36 + 8 - 6n + 6n$
$15n = 44$
$\dfrac{15n}{15} = \dfrac{44}{15}$
$n = 2\dfrac{14}{15}$

Find each product.

1. $5(2a + 3b)$
   $10a + 15b$

2. $3x(4x - 2y)$
   $12x^2 - 6xy$

3. $-4(a^2 - b^2)$
   $-4a^2 + 4b^2$

4. $8b\left(b^2 - \dfrac{1}{2}b\right)$
   $8b^3 - 4b^2$

5. $-5t^2\left(\dfrac{1}{25}t^2 - \dfrac{1}{25}t + \dfrac{1}{5}\right)$
   $-\dfrac{1}{5}t^4 + \dfrac{1}{5}t^3 - t^2$

6. $\left(\dfrac{1}{2}x + y\right)\left(\dfrac{1}{2}y\right)$
   $\dfrac{1}{4}xy + \dfrac{1}{2}y^2$

Simplify.

7. $4r(2r^2 - 3r + 5) + 6r(4r^2 + 2r + 8)$
   $32r^3 + 68r$

8. $2b(b^2 + 4b + 8) - 3b(3b^2 + 9b - 18)$
   $-7b^3 - 19b^2 + 70b$

Solve each equation.

9. $3(x + 5) - 6 = 18$
   3

10. $3x(x - 5) - 3x^2 = -30$
    2

11. $(4y - 3) - 8y + 6 = 19$
    -4

12. Ria's corn field has a perimeter of 18,000 meters. The length of one side is 3 meters less than twice the width. What are the dimensions of the field?
    5999 m × 3001 m

13. Three sides of a triangle have measures that are consecutive even integers. What are the lengths of the sides if the perimeter is 114 meters?
    36 m, 38 m, 40 m

Algebra 1

9-7

Study Guide

Multiplying Polynomials

The following example shows how the distributive property can
be used to multiply any two polynomials.

Example 1: Find $(2x - 6)(3x + 1)$.

$$\begin{array}{cccc} F & O & I & L \end{array}$$
$$(2x - 6)(3x + 1) = 2x \cdot 3x + 2x \cdot 1 + (-6) \cdot 3x + (-6) \cdot 1$$
$$= 6x^2 + 2x - 18x - 6$$
$$= 6x^2 - 16x - 6$$

You can also multiply polynomials vertically.

Example 2: Find $(3x^2 - x + 1)(5x + 2)$.

$$
\begin{array}{r}
3x^2 - x + 1 \\
\times \quad 5x + 2 \\
\hline
6x^2 - 2x + 2 \\
15x^3 - 5x^2 + 5x \\
\hline
15x^3 + x^2 + 3x + 2
\end{array}
$$

Multiply $3x^2 - x + 1$ by 2.

Multiply $3x^2 - x + 1$ by 5x.

Combine like terms.

Find each product.

1. $(5t + 4)(2t - 6)$

2. $(5m - 3n)(4m - 2n)$

3. $(a - 3b)(2a - 5b)$

4. $(3x - 0.1)(x + 0.1)$

5. $(8x + 5)(8x - 5)$

6. $(x + 5)(x + 2)$

7. $(2x - 4)(2x + 5)$

8. $\begin{array}{r} y^2 - 5y + 3 \\ \times \; 2y^2 + 7y - 4 \end{array}$

9. $\begin{array}{r} 3b^3 - 2b^2 + b \\ \times \quad 2b - 3 \end{array}$

Study Guide

Multiplying Polynomials

The following example shows how the distributive property can be used to multiply any two polynomials.

Example 1: Find $(2x - 6)(3x + 1)$.

$$\begin{array}{cccc} F & O & I & L \end{array}$$
$$(2x - 6)(3x + 1) = 2x \cdot 3x + 2x \cdot 1 + (-6) \cdot 3x + (-6) \cdot 1$$
$$= 6x^2 + 2x - 18x - 6$$
$$= 6x^2 - 16x - 6$$

You can also multiply polynomials vertically.

Example 2: Find $(3x^2 - x + 1)(5x + 2)$.

$$\begin{array}{r} 3x^2 - x + 1 \\ \times \quad 5x + 2 \\ \hline 6x^2 - 2x + 2 \\ 15x^3 - 5x^2 + 5x \quad\quad \\ \hline 15x^3 + x^2 + 3x + 2 \end{array}$$

Multiply $3x^2 - x + 1$ by 2.

Multiply $3x^2 - x + 1$ by 5x.

Combine like terms.

Find each product.

1. $(5t + 4)(2t - 6)$
$10t^2 - 22t - 24$

2. $(5m - 3n)(4m - 2n)$
$20m^2 - 22mn + 6n^2$

3. $(a - 3b)(2a - 5b)$
$2a^2 - 11ab + 15b^2$

4. $(3x - 0.1)(x + 0.1)$
$3x^2 + 0.2x - 0.01$

5. $(8x + 5)(8x - 5)$
$64x^2 - 25$

6. $(x + 5)(x + 2)$
$x^2 + 7x + 10$

7. $(2x - 4)(2x + 5)$
$4x^2 + 2x - 20$

8. $\begin{array}{r} y^2 - 5y + 3 \\ \times\ 2y^2 + 7y - 4 \end{array}$
$2y^4 - 3y^3 - 33y^2 + 41y - 12$

9. $\begin{array}{r} 3b^3 - 2b^2 + b \\ \times \quad 2b - 3 \end{array}$
$6b^4 - 13b^3 + 8b^2 - 3b$

Study Guide

Special Products

You can use the FOIL method to find some special products.

Square of a Sum	$(a + b)^2 = (a + b)(a + b) = a^2 + 2ab + b^2$
Square of a Difference	$(a - b)^2 = (a - b)(a - b) = a^2 - 2ab + b^2$
Difference of Squares	$(a + b)(a - b) = (a - b)(a + b) = a^2 - b^2$

Study the examples below.

Binomials	Product
$(3n + 4)^2$	$9n^2 + 24n + 16$
$(2z - 9)^2$	$4z^2 - 36z + 81$
$(5x - 3y)(5x + 3y)$	$25x^2 - 9y^2$

Find each product.

1. $(x - 6)^2$

2. $(3p + 4)^2$

3. $(x + 11)(x - 11)$

4. $(2x + 3)(2x - 3)$

5. $(4x - 5)^2$

6. $(9x - y)(9x + y)$

7. $(m + 5)^2$

8. $(8a - 7b)(8a + 7b)$

9. $(4a - 3b)^2$

10. $(3 - 5q)(3 + 5q)$

11. $(x^2 - 2)^2$

12. $(2.5 + q)^2$

13. $\left(\frac{3}{4}x + 1\right)\left(\frac{3}{4}x - 1\right)$

14. $(0.3p - 2q)^2$

15. $\left(\frac{1}{2}y + z\right)^2$

16. $(8 + x)^2$

17. $(6c - 10)(6c + 10)$

18. $(x^3 - 1)^2$

Study Guide

Special Products

You can use the FOIL method to find some special products.

Square of a Sum	$(a + b)^2 = (a + b)(a + b) = a^2 + 2ab + b^2$
Square of a Difference	$(a - b)^2 = (a - b)(a - b) = a^2 - 2ab + b^2$
Difference of Squares	$(a + b)(a - b) = (a - b)(a + b) = a^2 - b^2$

Study the examples below.

Binomials	Product
$(3n + 4)^2$	$9n^2 + 24n + 16$
$(2z - 9)^2$	$4z^2 - 36z + 81$
$(5x - 3y)(5x + 3y)$	$25x^2 - 9y^2$

Find each product.

1. $(x - 6)^2$
$x^2 - 12x + 36$

2. $(3p + 4)^2$
$9p^2 + 24p + 16$

3. $(x + 11)(x - 11)$
$x^2 - 121$

4. $(2x + 3)(2x - 3)$
$4x^2 - 9$

5. $(4x - 5)^2$
$16x^2 - 40x + 25$

6. $(9x - y)(9x + y)$
$81x^2 - y^2$

7. $(m + 5)^2$
$m^2 + 10m + 25$

8. $(8a - 7b)(8a + 7b)$
$64a^2 - 49b^2$

9. $(4a - 3b)^2$
$16a^2 - 24ab + 9b^2$

10. $(3 - 5q)(3 + 5q)$
$9 - 25q^2$

11. $(x^2 - 2)^2$
$x^4 - 4x^2 + 4$

12. $(2.5 + q)^2$
$6.25 + 5q + q^2$

13. $\left(\frac{3}{4}x + 1\right)\left(\frac{3}{4}x - 1\right)$
$\frac{9}{16}x^2 - 1$

14. $(0.3p - 2q)^2$
$0.09p^2 - 1.2pq + 4q^2$

15. $\left(\frac{1}{2}y + z\right)^2$
$\frac{1}{4}y^2 + yz + z^2$

16. $(8 + x)^2$
$64 + 16x + x^2$

17. $(6c - 10)(6c + 10)$
$36c^2 - 100$

18. $(x^3 - 1)^2$
$x^6 - 2x^3 + 1$

NAME_____ DATE _____

Study Guide

Factors and Greatest Common Factor

If two or more numbers are multiplied, each number is a **factor** of the product.

	Definition	Example
Prime Number	A *prime number* is a whole number, greater than 1, whose only factors are 1 and itself.	5
Composite Number	A *composite number* is a whole number, greater than 1, that is not prime.	10
Prime Factorization	*Prime factorization* occurs when a whole number is expressed as a product of factors that are all prime.	$45 = 3^2 \cdot 5$
Greatest Common Factor (GCF)	The *greatest common factor* of two or more integers is the greatest number that is a factor of the integers.	The GCF of 12 and 30 is 6.

The GCF of two or more monomials is the product of their common factors, when each monomial is expressed in factored form.

Example: Find the GCF of $16xy^2z^2$ and $72xyz^3$.

$$16xy^2z^2 = 2 \cdot 2 \cdot 2 \cdot 2 \cdot x \cdot y \cdot y \cdot z \cdot z$$
$$72xyz^3 = 2 \cdot 2 \cdot 2 \cdot 3 \cdot 3 \cdot x \cdot y \cdot z \cdot z \cdot z$$

The GCF of $16xy^2z^2$ and $72xyz^3$ is $2 \cdot 2 \cdot 2 \cdot x \cdot y \cdot z \cdot z$, or $8xyz^2$.

**State whether each number is prime or composite.
If the number is composite, find its prime factorization.**

1. 28

2. 61

3. 112

4. 2865

Factor each expression completely. Do not use exponents.

5. -34

6. -150

7. $56pq^3$

8. $-108(cd)^2$

Find the GCF of the given monomials.

9. $-45, 15$

10. $169, 13$

11. $-20, 440$

12. $49x, 343x^2$

13. $4a^7b, 28ab$

14. $96y, 12x, -8y$

NAME_____ DATE _____

Study Guide

Student Edition
Pages 558–563

Factors and Greatest Common Factor

If two or more numbers are multiplied, each number is a **factor** of the product.

	Definition	Example
Prime Number	A *prime number* is a whole number, greater than 1, whose only factors are 1 and itself.	5
Composite Number	A *composite number* is a whole number, greater than 1, that is not prime.	10
Prime Factorization	*Prime factorization* occurs when a whole number is expressed as a product of factors that are all prime.	$45 = 3^2 \cdot 5$
Greatest Common Factor (GCF)	The *greatest common factor* of two or more integers is the greatest number that is a factor of the integers.	The GCF of 12 and 30 is 6.

The GCF of two or more monomials is the product of their common factors, when each monomial is expressed in factored form.

Example: Find the GCF of $16xy^2z^2$ and $72xyz^3$.

$$16xy^2z^2 = \textcircled{2} \cdot \textcircled{2} \cdot \textcircled{2} \cdot 2 \cdot \textcircled{x} \cdot \textcircled{y} \cdot y \cdot \textcircled{z} \cdot \textcircled{z}$$

$$72xyz^3 = \textcircled{2} \cdot \textcircled{2} \cdot \textcircled{2} \cdot 3 \cdot 3 \cdot \textcircled{x} \cdot \textcircled{y} \cdot \textcircled{z} \cdot \textcircled{z} \cdot z$$

The GCF of $16xy^2z^2$ and $72xyz^3$ is $2 \cdot 2 \cdot 2 \cdot x \cdot y \cdot z \cdot z$, or $8xyz^2$.

State whether each number is _prime_ or _composite_.
If the number is composite, find its prime factorization.

1. 28 **composite;**
   $2^2 \cdot 7$

2. 61 **prime**

3. 112 **composite;**
   $2^4 \cdot 7$

4. 2865 **composite;**
   $3 \cdot 5 \cdot 191$

Factor each expression completely. Do not use exponents.

5. -34
   $-1 \cdot 2 \cdot 17$

6. -150
   $-1 \cdot 2 \cdot 3 \cdot 5 \cdot 5$

7. $56pq^3$
   $2 \cdot 2 \cdot 2 \cdot 7 \cdot p \cdot$
   $q \cdot q \cdot q$

8. $-108(cd)^2$
   $-1 \cdot 2 \cdot 2 \cdot 3 \cdot 3 \cdot$
   $3 \cdot c \cdot c \cdot d \cdot d$

Find the GCF of the given monomials.

9. $-45, 15$ **15**

10. $169, 13$ **13**

11. $-20, 440$ **20**

12. $49x, 343x^2$
    49x

13. $4a^7b, 28ab$
    4ab

14. $96y, 12x, -8y$
    4

Algebra 1

10-2

Study Guide

Factoring Using the Distributive Property

The distributive property has been used to multiply a polynomial by a monomial. It can also be used to express a polynomial in factored form. Compare the two columns in the table below.

Multiplying	Factoring
$3(a + b) = 3a + 3b$	$3a + 3b = 3(a + b)$
$x(y - z) = xy - xz$	$xy - xz = x(y - z)$
$6y(2x + 1) = 6y(2x) + 6y(1)$ $= 12xy + 6y$	$12xy + 6y = 2 \cdot 2 \cdot 3 \cdot x \cdot y + 2 \cdot 3 \cdot y$ $= 6y(2x) + 6y(1)$ $= 6y(2x + 1)$

Complete.

1. $9a + 18b = 9(\underline{\hspace{1cm}} + 2b)$

2. $12mn + 80m^2 = 4m(3n + \underline{\hspace{1cm}})$

3. $7c^3 - 7c^4 = 7c^3(\underline{\hspace{1cm}} - c)$

4. $4xy^3 + 16x^2y^2 = \underline{\hspace{1cm}}(y + 4x)$

Factor each polynomial.

5. $24x + 48y$

6. $30mn^2 + m^2n - 6n$

7. $q^4 - 18q^3 + 22q$

8. $a + 8a^2b - ab$

9. $55p^2 - 11p^7 + 44p^5$

10. $14c^3 - 42c^5 - 49c^4$

11. $4m + 6n - 8mn$

12. $14y^3 - 28y^2 + y$

13. $48w^2z + 18wz^2 - 36wz$

14. $9x^2 - 3x$

15. $96ab + 12a^2b - 84ab^3$

16. $45s^3 - 15s^2$

17. $18b^2a - 4ba + 7ab^2$

18. $12p^3q^2 - 18p^2q^2 + 30p$

19. $-x^5 - 4x^4 + 23x^3 - x$

Algebra 1

Study Guide

Factoring Using the Distributive Property

The distributive property has been used to multiply a polynomial by a monomial. It can also be used to express a polynomial in factored form. Compare the two columns in the table below.

Multiplying	Factoring
$3(a + b) = 3a + 3b$	$3a + 3b = 3(a + b)$
$x(y - z) = xy - xz$	$xy - xz = x(y - z)$
$6y(2x + 1) = 6y(2x) + 6y(1)$ $= 12xy + 6y$	$12xy + 6y = 2 \cdot 2 \cdot 3 \cdot x \cdot y + 2 \cdot 3 \cdot y$ $= 6y(2x) + 6y(1)$ $= 6y(2x + 1)$

Complete.

1. $9a + 18b = 9(\underline{\quad a \quad} + 2b)$

2. $12mn + 80m^2 = 4m(3n + \underline{\quad 20m \quad})$

3. $7c^3 - 7c^4 = 7c^3(\underline{\quad 1 \quad} - c)$

4. $4xy^3 + 16x^2y^2 = \underline{\quad 4xy^2 \quad}(y + 4x)$

Factor each polynomial.

5. $24x + 48y$
$24(x + 2y)$

6. $30mn^2 + m^2n - 6n$
$n(30mn + m^2 - 6)$

7. $q^4 - 18q^3 + 22q$
$q(q^3 - 18q^2 + 22)$

8. $a + 8a^2b - ab$
$a(1 + 8ab - b)$

9. $55p^2 - 11p^7 + 44p^5$
$11p^2(5 - p^5 + 4p^3)$

10. $14c^3 - 42c^5 - 49c^4$
$7c^3(2 - 6c^2 - 7c)$

11. $4m + 6n - 8mn$
$2(2m + 3n - 4mn)$

12. $14y^3 - 28y^2 + y$
$y(14y^2 - 28y + 1)$

13. $48w^2z + 18wz^2 - 36wz$
$6wz(8w + 3z - 6)$

14. $9x^2 - 3x$
$3x(3x - 1)$

15. $96ab + 12a^2b - 84ab^3$
$12ab(8 + a - 7b^2)$

16. $45s^3 - 15s^2$
$15s^2(3s - 1)$

17. $18b^2a - 4ba + 7ab^2$
$ab(25b - 4)$

18. $12p^3q^2 - 18p^2q^2 + 30p$
$6p(2p^2q^2 - 3pq^2 + 5)$

19. $-x^5 - 4x^4 + 23x^3 - x$
$x(-x^4 - 4x^3 + 23x^2 - 1)$

Algebra 1

Study Guide

Factoring Trinomials

To factor a trinomial of the form $ax^2 + bx + c$, follow Example 1 below.

Example 1: Factor $2d^2 + 15d + 18$.
The product of 2 and 18 is 36.
You need to find two integers whose *product* is 36 and whose *sum* is 15.

Factors of 36	Sum of Factors
1, 36	1 + 36 = 37
2, 18	2 + 18 = 20
3, 12	3 + 12 = 15

$$2d^2 + 15d + 18 = 2d^2 + (12 + 3)d + 18$$
$$= 2d^2 + 12d + 3d + 18$$
$$= (2d^2 + 12d) + (3d + 18)$$
$$= 2d(d + 6) + 3(d + 6) \quad \textbf{Factor the GCF from each group.}$$
$$= (2d + 3)(d + 6) \quad \textbf{Use the distributive property.}$$

To factor a trinomial of the form given above when $a = 1$, you need to find only the factors of c whose sum is b.

Example 2: Factor $x^2 + 7x + 10$.

Since 2 and 5 are factors of 10 whose sum is 7,
$x^2 + 7x + 10 = (x + 2)(x + 5)$.

The same pattern can be used to factor a trinomial $ax^2 + bx + c$ when $a = 1$ and c is negative. When this occurs, the factors of the trinomial are a *difference* and a *sum*.

Complete.

1. $x^2 - 5x - 14 = (x + \underline{\hspace{1cm}})(x - 7)$

2. $a^2 + 13a + 36 = (a + 9)(a \underline{\hspace{0.5cm}} 4)$

3. $p^2 - 25 = (p + 5)(p \underline{\hspace{0.5cm}} \underline{\hspace{0.5cm}})$

4. $x^2 - 6xy - 16y^2 = (x \underline{\hspace{0.5cm}} \underline{\hspace{0.5cm}})(x + 2y)$

5. $49 - n^2 = (7 \underline{\hspace{0.5cm}} \underline{\hspace{0.5cm}})(\underline{\hspace{0.5cm}} \underline{\hspace{0.5cm}} n)$

6. $a^4 + 3xa^2 - 10x^2 = (a^2 - \underline{\hspace{0.5cm}})(\underline{\hspace{0.5cm}} \underline{\hspace{0.5cm}} 5x)$

Factor each trinomial, if possible. If the trinomial cannot be factored using integers, write <u>prime</u>.

7. $y^2 + 12y + 32$

8. $x^2 - x - 6$

9. $x^2 - 4x - 21$

10. $y^2 + 22y + 121$

11. $9 - 7n + n^2$

12. $a^2 - 16a + 64$

13. $3x^2 + 2x - 8$

14. $18h^2 - 27h - 5$

15. $28x^2 + 60x - 25$

16. $48x^2 + 22x - 15$

17. $-4y^2 + 19y - 21$

18. $6a^2 - 7a + 18$

NAME_____ DATE _____

Study Guide

Factoring Trinomials

To factor a trinomial of the form $ax^2 + bx + c$, follow Example 1 below.

Example 1: Factor $2d^2 + 15d + 18$.
The product of 2 and 18 is 36.
You need to find two integers whose *product* is 36 and whose *sum* is 15.

Factors of 36	Sum of Factors
1, 36	1 + 36 = 37
2, 18	2 + 18 = 20
3, 12	3 + 12 = 15

$$2d^2 + 15d + 18 = 2d^2 + (12 + 3)d + 18$$
$$= 2d^2 + 12d + 3d + 18$$
$$= (2d^2 + 12d) + (3d + 18)$$
$$= 2d(d + 6) + 3(d + 6) \quad \text{Factor the GCF from each group.}$$
$$= (2d + 3)(d + 6) \quad \text{Use the distributive property.}$$

To factor a trinomial of the form given above when $a = 1$, you need to find only the factors of c whose sum is b.

Example 2: Factor $x^2 + 7x + 10$.

Since 2 and 5 are factors of 10 whose sum is 7,
$x^2 + 7x + 10 = (x + 2)(x + 5)$.

The same pattern can be used to factor a trinomial $ax^2 + bx + c$ when $a = 1$ and c is negative. When this occurs, the factors of the trinomial are a *difference* and a *sum*.

Complete.

1. $x^2 - 5x - 14 = (x + \underline{2})(x - 7)$

2. $a^2 + 13a + 36 = (a + 9)(a \underline{+} 4)$

3. $p^2 - 25 = (p + 5)(p \underline{- 5})$

4. $x^2 - 6xy - 16y^2 = (x \underline{- 8y})(x + 2y)$

5. $49 - n^2 = (7 \underline{+ n})(7 \underline{-} n)$

6. $a^4 + 3xa^2 - 10x^2 = (a^2 - \underline{2x})(a^2 \underline{+} 5x)$

Factor each trinomial, if possible. If the trinomial cannot be factored using integers, write <u>prime</u>.

7. $y^2 + 12y + 32$
$(y + 4)(y + 8)$

8. $x^2 - x - 6$
$(x - 3)(x + 2)$

9. $x^2 - 4x - 21$
$(x - 7)(x + 3)$

10. $y^2 + 22y + 121$
$(y + 11)(y + 11)$

11. $9 - 7n + n^2$
prime

12. $a^2 - 16a + 64$
$(a - 8)(a - 8)$

13. $3x^2 + 2x - 8$
$(3x - 4)(x + 2)$

14. $18h^2 - 27h - 5$
$(3h - 5)(6h + 1)$

15. $28x^2 + 60x - 25$
$(2x + 5)(14x - 5)$

16. $48x^2 + 22x - 15$
$(6x + 5)(8x - 3)$

17. $-4y^2 + 19y - 21$
$(4y - 7)(3 - y)$

18. $6a^2 - 7a + 18$
prime

 Algebra 1

Study Guide

Factoring Differences of Squares

Use the difference of squares to factor polynomials.

Difference of Squares	$a^2 - b^2 = (a - b)(a + b) = (a + b)(a - b)$

Example 1: Factor $4y^2 - 81z^2$.

$$4y^2 - 81z^2 = (2y)^2 - (9z)^2$$
$$= (2y - 9z)(2y + 9z)$$

$2y \cdot 2y = 4y^2$ and $9z \cdot 9z = 81z^2$

Use the difference of squares.

In some binomials you have to factor a GCF before you can factor the difference of squares.

Example 2: Factor $50a^2 - 72$.

$$50a^2 - 72 = 2(25a^2 - 36)$$
$$= 2(5a - 6)(5a + 6)$$

The GCF is 2.

Use the difference of squares.

State whether each binomial can be factored as a difference of squares.

1. $a^2 - b^2$

2. $x^2 + y^2$

3. $a^2 - 36$

4. $2p - \dfrac{1}{9}$

5. $\dfrac{1}{2}m^2 + \dfrac{1}{4}n^2$

6. $\dfrac{49}{289}x^2 - 1$

7. $0.16m^2 + 0.25n^2$

8. $225b^2 - a^2$

9. $a - 16$

10. $15x^2 + 5$

11. $9y^2 - 4x^2$

12. $-p^2 + 9q^2$

Factor each polynomial, if possible. If the polynomial cannot be factored, write __prime__.

13. $m^2 - 16n^2$

14. $4a^2 - 9b^2$

15. $x^2 - 64$

16. $-81 + a^4$

17. $m^6 - 16n^4$

18. $-2 + 2y^2$

19. $p^2q^2 - \dfrac{1}{16}$

20. $\dfrac{1}{4}z^4 - 25$

21. $\dfrac{2}{3}x^2 - 9$

22. $12x^2 - 27y^2$

23. $6 - 54z^2$

24. $(x + y)^2 - w^2$

25. $3x^4 - 75$

26. $(n + 7)^2 - 1$

27. $2p^4 - 32q^4$

NAME_____ DATE _____

Study Guide

Factoring Differences of Squares

Use the difference of squares to factor polynomials.

Difference of Squares	$a^2 - b^2 = (a - b)(a + b) = (a + b)(a - b)$

Example 1: Factor $4y^2 - 81z^2$.

$$4y^2 - 81z^2 = (2y)^2 - (9z)^2 \qquad \text{2y · 2y = 4y}^2 \text{ and 9z · 9z = 81z}^2$$
$$= (2y - 9z)(2y + 9z) \qquad \text{Use the difference of squares.}$$

In some binomials you have to factor a GCF before you can factor the difference of squares.

Example 2: Factor $50a^2 - 72$.

$$50a^2 - 72 = 2(25a^2 - 36) \qquad \text{The GCF is 2.}$$
$$= 2(5a - 6)(5a + 6) \qquad \text{Use the difference of squares.}$$

State whether each binomial can be factored as a difference of squares.

1. $a^2 - b^2$ **yes**   2. $x^2 + y^2$ **no**   3. $a^2 - 36$ **yes**   4. $2p - \dfrac{1}{9}$ **no**

5. $\dfrac{1}{2}m^2 + \dfrac{1}{4}n^2$ **no**   6. $\dfrac{49}{289}x^2 - 1$ **yes**   7. $0.16m^2 + 0.25n^2$ **no**   8. $225b^2 - a^2$ **yes**

9. $a - 16$ **no**   10. $15x^2 + 5$ **no**   11. $9y^2 - 4x^2$ **yes**   12. $-p^2 + 9q^2$ **yes**

Factor each polynomial, if possible. If the polynomial cannot be factored, write _prime_.

13. $m^2 - 16n^2$
$(m - 4n)(m + 4n)$

14. $4a^2 - 9b^2$
$(2a + 3b)(2a - 3b)$

15. $x^2 - 64$
$(x - 8)(x + 8)$

16. $-81 + a^4$
$(a - 3)(a + 3)(a^2 + 9)$

17. $m^6 - 16n^4$
$(m^3 - 4n^2)(m^3 + 4n^2)$

18. $-2 + 2y^2$
$2(y - 1)(y + 1)$

19. $p^2q^2 - \dfrac{1}{16}$
$\left(pq - \dfrac{1}{4}\right)\left(pq + \dfrac{1}{4}\right)$

20. $\dfrac{1}{4}z^4 - 25$
$\left(\dfrac{1}{2}z^2 - 5\right)\left(\dfrac{1}{2}z^2 + 5\right)$

21. $\dfrac{2}{3}x^2 - 9$ **prime**

22. $12x^2 - 27y^2$
$3(2x - 3y)(2x + 3y)$

23. $6 - 54z^2$
$6(1 + 3z)(1 - 3z)$

24. $(x + y)^2 - w^2$
$(x + y - w)(x + y + w)$

25. $3x^4 - 75$
$3(x^2 - 5)(x^2 + 5)$

26. $(n + 7)^2 - 1$
$(n + 6)(n + 8)$

27. $2p^4 - 32q^4$
$2(p - 2q)(p + 2q)(p^2 + 4q^2)$

       Algebra 1

10-5

Study Guide

Perfect Squares and Factoring

Perfect Square Trinomials	$(a + b)^2 = a^2 + 2ab + b^2$
	$(a - b)^2 = a^2 - 2ab + b^2$

To factor a perfect square trinomial, the first and last terms must be perfect squares, and the middle term must be twice the product of the square roots of the first and last terms.

Example: Factor $m^2 + 26m + 169$.
$$m^2 + 26m + 169 = (m)^2 + 2(m)(13) + (13)^2$$
$$= (m + 13)^2$$

To determine whether a trinomial in mixed order is a perfect square, first arrange the terms in order of descending powers.

Determine whether each trinomial is a perfect square trinomial. If so, factor it.

1. $y^2 + 10y + 25$

2. $m^2 - 14mn + 49n^2$

3. $p^2 + 8p + 64$

Factor each polynomial, if possible. If the polynomial cannot be factored, write _prime_.

4. $16x^2 + 48x + 36$

5. $49a^4 - 112a^2b^2 + 64b^4$

6. $x^2y^2 - 6abxy + 9a^2b^2$

7. $81 + 18xy + x^2y^2$

8. $25x^2 - 10x - 1$

9. $169 - 26r + r^2$

10. $7x^2 - 9x + 2$

11. $a^2 + 22a + 121$

12. $9x^2 - 12x + 4$

13. $x^2 - 9x - 81$

14. $49b^2 - 126ab + 81a^2$

15. $144 + 24x + x^2$

16. $256 - 16b + b^2$

17. $361 - 38x + x^2$

18. $16a^2 - 40ab + 25b^2$

19. $36x^2 - 12x + 1$

20. $9x^2 + 66x + 121y^2$

21. $4a^2 - 20a + 25$

Algebra 1

10-5

Study Guide

Perfect Squares and Factoring

Perfect Square Trinomials	$(a + b)^2 = a^2 + 2ab + b^2$
	$(a - b)^2 = a^2 - 2ab + b^2$

To factor a perfect square trinomial, the first and last terms must be perfect squares, and the middle term must be twice the product of the square roots of the first and last terms.

Example: Factor $m^2 + 26m + 169$.
$$m^2 + 26m + 169 = (m)^2 + 2(m)(13) + (13)^2$$
$$= (m + 13)^2$$

To determine whether a trinomial in mixed order is a perfect square, first arrange the terms in order of descending powers.

Determine whether each trinomial is a perfect square trinomial. If so, factor it.

1. $y^2 + 10y + 25$
   yes; $(y + 5)^2$

2. $m^2 - 14mn + 49n^2$
   yes; $(m - 7n)^2$

3. $p^2 + 8p + 64$ **no**

Factor each polynomial, if possible. If the polynomial cannot be factored, write _prime_.

4. $16x^2 + 48x + 36$
   $4(2x + 3)^2$

5. $49a^4 - 112a^2b^2 + 64b^4$
   $(7a^2 - 8b^2)^2$

6. $x^2y^2 - 6abxy + 9a^2b^2$
   $(xy - 3ab)^2$

7. $81 + 18xy + x^2y^2$
   $(9 + xy)^2$

8. $25x^2 - 10x - 1$
   prime

9. $169 - 26r + r^2$
   $(13 - r)^2$

10. $7x^2 - 9x + 2$
    $(7x - 2)(x - 1)$

11. $a^2 + 22a + 121$
    $(a + 11)^2$

12. $9x^2 - 12x + 4$
    $(3x - 2)^2$

13. $x^2 - 9x - 81$
    prime

14. $49b^2 - 126ab + 81a^2$
    $(7b - 9a)^2$

15. $144 + 24x + x^2$
    $(12 + x)^2$

16. $256 - 16b + b^2$
    prime

17. $361 - 38x + x^2$
    $(19 - x)^2$

18. $16a^2 - 40ab + 25b^2$
    $(4a - 5b)^2$

19. $36x^2 - 12x + 1$
    $(6x - 1)^2$

20. $9x^2 + 66x + 121y^2$
    prime

21. $4a^2 - 20a + 25$
    $(2a - 5)^2$

10-6

Study Guide

Solving Equations by Factoring

Factoring can be used to solve many kinds of problems.

Example: A rocket is fired with an initial velocity of 2288 feet per second. How many seconds will it take for the rocket to hit the ground?

Explore Use the formula $h = vt - 16t^2$.

Plan Substitute the appropriate values into the formula.

Solve $0 = 2288t - 16t^2$
$0 = 16t(143 - t)$
$16t = 0$ or $143 - t = 0$ **Zero product property**
$t = 0$ $143 = t$

Examine An answer of 0 seconds is not a reasonable answer, so use only the value 143. The rocket returns to the ground in 143 seconds.

Solve each equation. Check your solutions.

1. $n^2 - 16 = 0$

2. $x^2 + 10x + 25 = 0$

3. $9x^2 + x = 0$

4. $x^2 = 24 - 10x$

5. $x^3 - 18x = 7x^2$

6. $x^3 - 36x = 9x^2$

For each problem below, define a variable. Then use an equation to solve the problem. Disregard any unreasonable solutions.

7. The difference of the squares of two consecutive odd integers is 24. Find the integers.

8. The length of a Charlotte, North Carolina, conservatory garden is 20 yards greater than its width. The area is 300 square yards. What are the dimensions?

Use the formula $h = vt - 16t^2$ to solve each problem.

9. A punter can kick a football with an initial velocity of 48 feet per second. How many seconds will it take the ball to return to the ground?

10. If a rocket is launched at Houston, Texas, with an initial velocity of 1600 feet per second, when will the rocket be 14,400 feet high?

Study Guide

Solving Equations by Factoring

Factoring can be used to solve many kinds of problems.

Example: A rocket is fired with an initial velocity of 2288 feet per second. How many seconds will it take for the rocket to hit the ground?

Explore Use the formula $h = vt - 16t^2$.

Plan Substitute the appropriate values into the formula.

Solve $0 = 2288t - 16t^2$
$0 = 16t(143 - t)$
$16t = 0$ or $143 - t = 0$ **Zero product property**
$t = 0$ $143 = t$

Examine An answer of 0 seconds is not a reasonable answer, so use only the value 143. The rocket returns to the ground in 143 seconds.

Solve each equation. Check your solutions.

1. $n^2 - 16 = 0$
$\{-4, 4\}$

2. $x^2 + 10x + 25 = 0$
$\{-5\}$

3. $9x^2 + x = 0$
$\left\{-\dfrac{1}{9}, 0\right\}$

4. $x^2 = 24 - 10x$
$\{-12, 2\}$

5. $x^3 - 18x = 7x^2$
$\{-2, 0, 9\}$

6. $x^3 - 36x = 9x^2$
$\{-3, 0, 12\}$

For each problem below, define a variable. Then use an equation to solve the problem. Disregard any unreasonable solutions.

7. The difference of the squares of two consecutive odd integers is 24. Find the integers. $-5, -7$ or $5, 7$

8. The length of a Charlotte, North Carolina, conservatory garden is 20 yards greater than its width. The area is 300 square yards. What are the dimensions?
30 yards by 10 yards

Use the formula $h = vt - 16t^2$ to solve each problem.

9. A punter can kick a football with an initial velocity of 48 feet per second. How many seconds will it take the ball to return to the ground?
3 seconds

10. If a rocket is launched from Houston, Texas, with an initial velocity of 1600 feet per second, when will the rocket be 14,400 feet high?
at 10 seconds and 90 seconds

NAME_____ DATE _____

Study Guide

Student Edition
Pages 611–617

Graphing Quadratic Functions

An equation such as $y = x^2 - 4x + 1$ describes a type of function known as a **quadratic function.**

Definition of Quadratic Function
A quadratic function is a function that can be described by an equation of the form $y = ax^2 + bx + c$, where $a \neq 0$.

Graphs of quadratic functions have certain common characteristics. They have a general shape called a **parabola.** They have a minimum or maximum point. In general, a parabola will open upward and have a minimum point when the coefficient of y and x^2 have the same sign. It will open downward and have a maximum point when the coefficient of y and x^2 are opposite in sign. The vertical line containing the minimum or maximum point is the **axis of symmetry.** The minimum or maximum point is called the **vertex** of the parabola.

Equation of Axis of Symmetry
The equation of the axis of symmetry of $y = ax^2 + bx + c$, where $a \neq 0$ is $$x = -\frac{b}{2a}.$$

Write the equation of the axis of symmetry and find the coordinates of the vertex of the graph of each equation. Then graph the equation.

1. $y = x^2 + 3x$

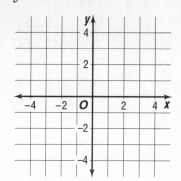

2. $y = 3x^2 + x + 1$

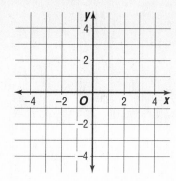

3. $y = -x^2 - 4$

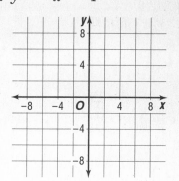

4. $y = -\frac{1}{2}x^2 + x + \frac{5}{2}$

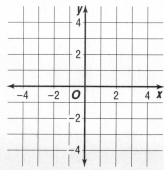

5. $y = -x^2 - 6x - 7$

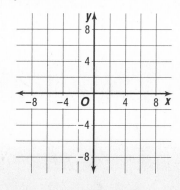

6. $y = 2x^2 + 12x + 9$

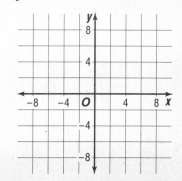

Algebra 1

11-1

Study Guide

Graphing Quadratic Functions

An equation such as $y = x^2 - 4x + 1$ describes a type of function known as a **quadratic function.**

Definition of Quadratic Function
A quadratic function is a function that can be described by an equation of the form $y = ax^2 + bx + c$, where $a \neq 0$.

Graphs of quadratic functions have certain common characteristics. They have a general shape called a **parabola.** They have a minimum or maximum point. In general, a parabola will open upward and have a minimum point when the coefficient of y and x^2 have the same sign. It will open downward and have a maximum point when the coefficient of y and x^2 are opposite in sign. The vertical line containing the minimum or maximum point is the **axis of symmetry.** The minimum or maximum point is called the **vertex** of the parabola.

Equation of Axis of Symmetry
The equation of the axis of symmetry of $y = ax^2 + bx + c$, where $a \neq 0$ is $$x = -\frac{b}{2a}.$$

Write the equation of the axis of symmetry and find the coordinates of the vertex of the graph of each equation. Then graph the equation.

1. $y = x^2 + 3x$

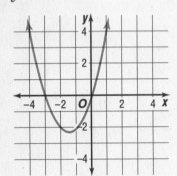

$$x = -\frac{3}{2}; \left(-\frac{3}{2}, -\frac{9}{4}\right)$$

2. $y = 3x^2 + x + 1$

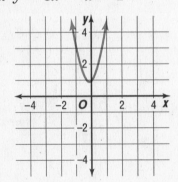

$$x = -\frac{1}{6}; \left(-\frac{1}{6}, \frac{11}{12}\right)$$

3. $y = -x^2 - 4$

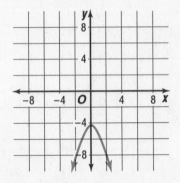

$$x = 0; (0, -4)$$

4. $y = -\frac{1}{2}x^2 + x + \frac{5}{2}$

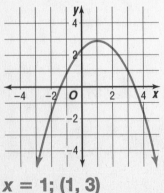

$$x = 1; (1, 3)$$

5. $y = -x^2 - 6x - 7$

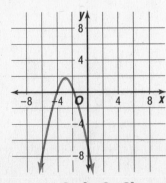

$$x = -3; (-3, 2)$$

6. $y = 2x^2 + 12x + 9$

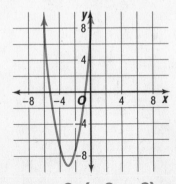

$$x = -3; (-3, -9)$$

Algebra 1

11-2

Study Guide

Student Edition
Pages 620–627

Solving Quadratic Equations by Graphing

A **quadratic equation** is an equation in which the value of the related quadratic function is 0. The solutions of a quadratic equation are called the **roots** of the equation. The roots of a quadratic equation can be found by graphing the related quadratic function and finding the *x*-intercepts or **zeros** of the function.

Examples: Solve each equation by graphing. If exact roots cannot be found, estimate the roots by stating the consecutive integers between which the roots lie.

a. $x^2 + 7x + 12 = 0$

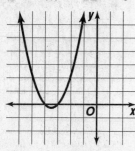

-3 and -4

b. $x^2 + 6x + 6 = 0$

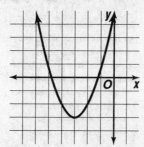

between -5 and -4 and between -2 and -1

c. $x^2 - 4x + 5$

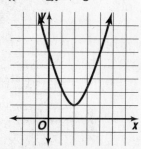

no real roots

Solve each equation by graphing. If exact roots cannot be found, state the consecutive integers between which the roots lie.

1. $x^2 - x - 12 = 0$

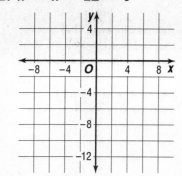

2. $x^2 + 4 = 0$

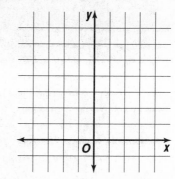

3. $4x^2 - 12x + 3 = 0$

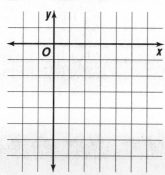

4. $4x^2 = 35 - 4x$

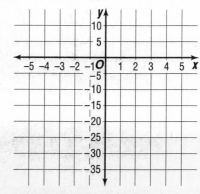

Solving Quadratic Equations by Graphing

A **quadratic equation** is an equation in which the value of the related quadratic function is 0. The solutions of a quadratic equation are called the **roots** of the equation. The roots of a quadratic equation can be found by graphing the related quadratic function and finding the x-intercepts or **zeros** of the function.

Examples: Solve each equation by graphing. If exact roots cannot be found, estimate the roots by stating the consecutive integers between which the roots lie.

a. $x^2 + 7x + 12 = 0$

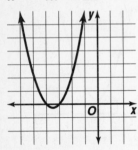

-3 and -4

b. $x^2 + 6x + 6 = 0$

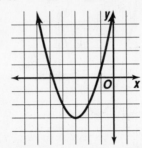

between -5 and -4 and between -2 and -1

c. $x^2 - 4x + 5$

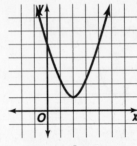

no real roots

Solve each equation by graphing. If exact roots cannot be found, state the consecutive integers between which the roots lie.

1. $x^2 - x - 12 = 0$ **4, −3**

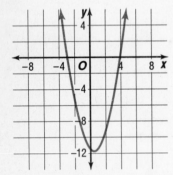

2. $x^2 + 4 = 0$ **no real roots**

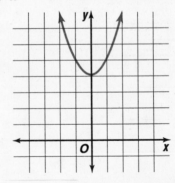

3. $4x^2 - 12x + 3 = 0$ **between 0 and 1 and 2 and 3**

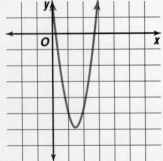

4. $4x^2 = 35 - 4x$ **between −3 and −4 and 2 and 3**

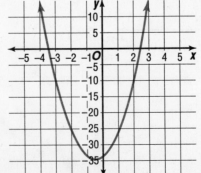

Study Guide

Student Edition
Pages 628–633

Solving Quadratic Equations by Using the Quadratic Formula

The method of completing the square can be used to develop a general formula called the *quadratic formula* that can be used to solve any quadratic equation.

The Quadratic Formula
The roots of a quadratic equation of the form $ax^2 + bx + c = 0$, where $a \neq 0$, are given by the formula $$x = \frac{-b \pm \sqrt{b^2 - 4ac}}{2a}.$$

In order to find a real value for $\sqrt{b^2 - 4ac}$, the value of $b^2 - 4ac$ must be nonnegative. If $b^2 - 4ac$ is negative, the equation has no real roots.

Example: Use the quadratic formula to solve $x^2 - 6x - 2 = 0$.

$$x = \frac{-b \pm \sqrt{b^2 - 4ac}}{2a}$$

$$= \frac{6 \pm \sqrt{(-6)^2 - 4(1)(-2)}}{2(1)} \qquad a = 1, b = -6, \text{ and } c = -2$$

$$= \frac{6 \pm \sqrt{44}}{2}$$

$$x \approx 6.32 \text{ or } x \approx -0.32$$

The two roots are approximately 6.32 and -0.32.

Solve each equation by using the quadratic formula.
Approximate irrational roots to the nearest hundredth.

1. $4t^2 = 144$

2. $2x^2 + 9x + 4 = 0$

3. $8x^2 + 17x + 2 = 0$

4. $3z^2 + 5z - 2 = 0$

5. $-2m^2 + 8m + 4 = 0$

6. $x^2 + 3x - 2 = 0$

7. $2x^2 - 6x + 4 = 0$

8. $5x^2 + 10 = 15$

9. $2y^2 - 9y - 3 = 0$

NAME_____ DATE _____

Study Guide

Solving Quadratic Equations by Using the Quadratic Formula

The method of completing the square can be used to develop a general formula called the *quadratic formula* that can be used to solve any quadratic equation.

The Quadratic Formula
The roots of a quadratic equation of the form $ax^2 + bx + c = 0$, where $a \neq 0$, are given by the formula $$x = \frac{-b \pm \sqrt{b^2 - 4ac}}{2a}.$$

In order to find a real value for $\sqrt{b^2 - 4ac}$, the value of $b^2 - 4ac$ must be nonnegative. If $b^2 - 4ac$ is negative, the equation has no real roots.

Example: Use the quadratic formula to solve $x^2 - 6x - 2 = 0$.

$$x = \frac{-b \pm \sqrt{b^2 - 4ac}}{2a}$$

$$= \frac{6 \pm \sqrt{(-6)^2 - 4(1)(-2)}}{2(1)} \qquad a = 1, b = -6, \text{ and } c = -2$$

$$= \frac{6 \pm \sqrt{44}}{2}$$

$$x \approx 6.32 \text{ or } x \approx -0.32$$

The two roots are approximately 6.32 and -0.32.

Solve each equation by using the quadratic formula. Approximate irrational roots to the nearest hundredth.

1. $4t^2 = 144$
−6, 6

2. $2x^2 + 9x + 4 = 0$
$-4, -\dfrac{1}{2}$

3. $8x^2 + 17x + 2 = 0$
$-2, -\dfrac{1}{8}$

4. $3z^2 + 5z - 2 = 0$
$-2, \dfrac{1}{3}$

5. $-2m^2 + 8m + 4 = 0$
4.45, −0.45

6. $x^2 + 3x - 2 = 0$
0.56, −3.56

7. $2x^2 - 6x + 4 = 0$
1, 2

8. $5x^2 + 10 = 15$
−1, 1

9. $2y^2 - 9y - 3 = 0$
4.81, −0.31

NAME_____ DATE _____

Study Guide

Exponential Functions

An equation in the form $y = a^x$, where $a > 0$ and $a \neq 1$, is called an **exponential function.** You can use a calculator to evaluate exponential expressions.

Example: Use a calculator to approximate $0.5^{-3.5} + 2$ to the nearest hundredth.

ENTER: 0.5 $\boxed{y^x}$ 3.5 $\boxed{+/-}$ $\boxed{=}$ $\boxed{+}$ 2 $\boxed{=}$ 13.3137085

$0.5^{-3.5} + 2 \approx 13.31$

You can use values of exponential expressions to find ordered pairs that satisfy an exponential function. Then you can use the ordered pairs to graph the function.

Example: Graph $y = \left(\frac{1}{2}\right)^x$.

x	y
−2	4
−1	2
0	1
1	0.5
2	0.25

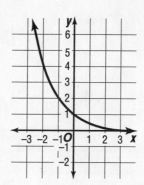

Graph each function.

1. $y = 0.3^x$

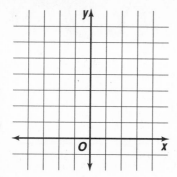

2. $y = 3^x + 1$

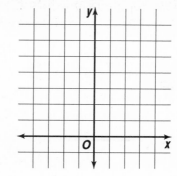

3. $y = 3^{2x-1}$

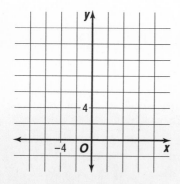

4. $y = \left(\frac{1}{2}\right)^x - 2$

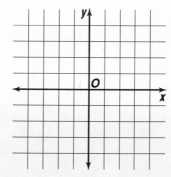

Algebra 1

NAME_____ DATE _____

Study Guide

Exponential Functions

An equation in the form $y = a^x$, where $a > 0$ and $a \neq 1$, is called an **exponential function.** You can use a calculator to evaluate exponential expressions.

Example: Use a calculator to approximate $0.5^{-3.5} + 2$ to the nearest hundredth.

ENTER: 0.5 $\boxed{y^x}$ 3.5 $\boxed{+/-}$ $\boxed{=}$ $\boxed{+}$ 2 $\boxed{=}$ 13.3137085

$0.5^{-3.5} + 2 \approx 13.31$

You can use values of exponential expressions to find ordered pairs that satisfy an exponential function. Then you can use the ordered pairs to graph the function.

Example: Graph $y = \left(\frac{1}{2}\right)^x$.

x	y
−2	4
−1	2
0	1
1	0.5
2	0.25

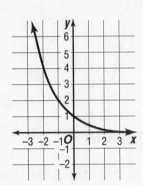

Graph each function.

1. $y = 0.3^x$

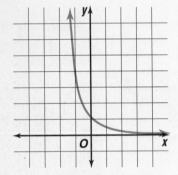

2. $y = 3^x + 1$

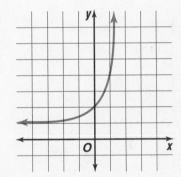

3. $y = 3^{2x-1}$

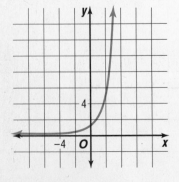

4. $y = \left(\frac{1}{2}\right)^x - 2$

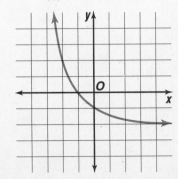

Algebra 1

Study Guide

Growth and Decay

Population increases and monetary investments are examples of **exponential growth.** This means that an initial amount increases at a steady rate over a period of time.

Radioactive decay and depreciation are examples of **exponential decay.** This means that an initial amount decreases at a steady rate over a period of time.

General Formula for Exponential Growth
$A = C(1 + r)^t$,
where C is the initial amount, r is the rate of increase (a percent written as a decimal), t is time, and A is the final amount.

General Formula for Exponential Decay
$A = C(1 - r)^t$,
where C is the initial amount, r is the rate of decrease (a percent written as a decimal), t is time, and A is the final amount.

Example 1: The population of Johnson City has grown at a rate of 3.2% each year for the last 10 years. If the population 10 years ago was 25,000, what is the population today?

$A = C(1 + r)^t$
$\quad = 25,000(1 + 0.032)^{10}$ **3.2% = 0.032**
$\quad \approx 34,256$ **Use a calculator.**

Example 2: A tractor has a depreciation rate of 19% per year. If the original price of the tractor was $29,000, what is the value of the tractor 5 years later?

$A = C(1 - r)^t$
$\quad = \$29,000(1 - 0.19)^5$ **19% = 0.19**
$\quad \approx \$10,111.68$ **Use a calculator.**

Solve.

1. The formula for compound interest is $A = P\left(1 + \dfrac{r}{n}\right)^{nt}$, where P is the initial amount invested, r is the annual rate of interest, n is the number of times a year the interest is compounded, and t is the number of years. If $100,000 is invested in an account that pays 5.2% compounded quarterly, how much money will be in the account after 12 years?

2. Carl Gossell is a machinist. He bought some new machinery for $125,000. He wants to calculate the value of the machinery over the next 10 years for tax purposes. If the machinery depreciates at 15% per year, what is the value of the machinery (to the nearest $100) at the end of 10 years?

NAME _____ DATE _____

Study Guide

Growth and Decay

Population increases and monetary investments are examples of **exponential growth.** This means that an initial amount increases at a steady rate over a period of time.

Radioactive decay and depreciation are examples of **exponential decay.** This means that an initial amount decreases at a steady rate over a period of time.

General Formula for Exponential Growth
$A = C(1 + r)^t$,
where C is the initial amount, r is the rate of increase (a percent written as a decimal), t is time, and A is the final amount.

General Formula for Exponential Decay
$A = C(1 - r)^t$,
where C is the initial amount, r is the rate of decrease (a percent written as a decimal), t is time, and A is the final amount.

Example 1: The population of Johnson City has grown at a rate of 3.2% each year for the last 10 years. If the population 10 years ago was 25,000, what is the population today?

$A = C(1 + r)^t$

$= 25,000(1 + 0.032)^{10}$ **3.2% = 0.032**

$\approx 34,256$ **Use a calculator.**

Example 2: A tractor has a depreciation rate of 19% per year. If the original price of the tractor was $29,000, what is the value of the tractor 5 years later?

$A = C(1 - r)^t$

$= \$29,000(1 - 0.19)^5$ **19% = 0.19**

$\approx \$10,111.68$ **Use a calculator.**

Solve.

1. The formula for compound interest is $A = P\left(1 + \dfrac{r}{n}\right)^{nt}$, where P is the initial amount invested, r is the annual rate of interest, n is the number of times a year the interest is compounded, and t is the number of years. If $100,000 is invested in an account that pays 5.2% compounded quarterly, how much money will be in the account after 12 years? **$185,888.87**

2. Carl Gossell is a machinist. He bought some new machinery for $125,000. He wants to calculate the value of the machinery over the next 10 years for tax purposes. If the machinery depreciates at 15% per year, what is the value of the machinery (to the nearest $100) at the end of 10 years? **$24,600**

Simplifying Rational Expressions

Factoring polynomials is a useful tool for simplifying fractions or **rational expressions.**

To simplify a rational number such as $\frac{9}{21}$, first factor the numerator and denominator. Then divide each by the greatest common factor.

$$\frac{9}{21} = \frac{3 \cdot 3}{7 \cdot 3}$$ **The greatest common factor is 3.**

$$= \frac{3 \cdot \cancel{3}}{7 \cdot \cancel{3}} \text{ or } \frac{3}{7}$$ **Notice that $\frac{3}{3} = 1$.**

The procedure can be used to simplify rational expressions.

Example 1: Simplify $\frac{54z^3}{24yz}$.

$$\frac{54z^3}{24yz} = \frac{2 \cdot 3 \cdot 3 \cdot 3 \cdot z \cdot z \cdot z}{2 \cdot 2 \cdot 2 \cdot 3 \cdot y \cdot z}$$

$$= \frac{\cancel{2} \cdot \cancel{3} \cdot 3 \cdot 3 \cdot \cancel{z} \cdot z \cdot z}{\cancel{2} \cdot 2 \cdot 2 \cdot \cancel{3} \cdot y \cdot \cancel{z}} = \frac{9z^2}{4y}$$

The excluded value of y and z is 0.

Example 2: Simplify $\frac{x + 3}{x^2 - 9}$.

$$\frac{x + 3}{x^2 - 9} = \frac{(x + 3) \cdot 1}{(x + 3)(x - 3)}$$

$$= \frac{\cancel{(x + 3)} \cdot 1}{\cancel{(x + 3)}(x - 3)} = \frac{1}{x - 3}$$

The excluded values of x are 3 and -3.

Simplify each rational expression. State the excluded values of the variables.

1. $\dfrac{a^3}{4a^6}$

2. $\dfrac{7n^3}{21n^8}$

3. $\dfrac{6}{2x^2 + 4}$

4. $\dfrac{2b(x + 1)}{4b(x - 1)}$

5. $\dfrac{12x}{8(x + 1)}$

6. $\dfrac{4a(x + 1)}{2a}$

7. $\dfrac{x^2 + 5x + 6}{x + 3}$

8. $\dfrac{x^2 - 2x - 3}{x^2 - 1}$

9. $\dfrac{x + 8}{x^2 + 11x + 24}$

10. $\dfrac{3a^5b^2}{18a^5b^3}$

11. $\dfrac{6x^2 + 7x + 2}{4x^2 - 1}$

12. $\dfrac{4x - 4}{7x - 7}$

13. $\dfrac{x + 1}{x^3 - x}$

14. $\dfrac{6x - 30}{x^2 - 7x + 10}$

NAME_____ DATE _____

Study Guide

Simplifying Rational Expressions

Factoring polynomials is a useful tool for simplifying fractions or **rational expressions.**

To simplify a rational number such as $\dfrac{9}{21}$, first factor the numerator and denominator. Then divide each by the greatest common factor.

$\dfrac{9}{21} = \dfrac{3 \cdot 3}{7 \cdot 3}$ **The greatest common factor is 3.**

$= \dfrac{3 \cdot \cancel{3}}{7 \cdot \cancel{3}}$ or $\dfrac{3}{7}$ **Notice that $\dfrac{3}{3} = 1$.**

The procedure can be used to simplify rational expressions.

Example 1: Simplify $\dfrac{54z^3}{24yz}$.

$\dfrac{54z^3}{24yz} = \dfrac{2 \cdot 3 \cdot 3 \cdot 3 \cdot z \cdot z \cdot z}{2 \cdot 2 \cdot 2 \cdot 3 \cdot y \cdot z}$

$= \dfrac{\cancel{2} \cdot 3 \cdot 3 \cdot 3 \cdot \cancel{z} \cdot z \cdot z}{\cancel{2} \cdot 2 \cdot 2 \cdot \cancel{3} \cdot y \cdot \cancel{z}} = \dfrac{9z^2}{4y}$

The excluded value of y and z is 0.

Example 2: Simplify $\dfrac{x + 3}{x^2 - 9}$.

$\dfrac{x + 3}{x^2 - 9} = \dfrac{(x + 3) \cdot 1}{(x + 3)(x - 3)}$

$= \dfrac{\cancel{(x + 3)} \cdot 1}{\cancel{(x + 3)}(x - 3)} = \dfrac{1}{x - 3}$

The excluded values of x are 3 and -3.

Simplify each rational expression. State the excluded values of the variables.

1. $\dfrac{a^3}{4a^6}\ \dfrac{1}{4a^3}, a \neq 0$

2. $\dfrac{7n^3}{21n^8}\ \dfrac{1}{3n^5}, n \neq 0$

3. $\dfrac{6}{2x^2 + 4}\ \dfrac{3}{x^2 + 2}$

4. $\dfrac{2b(x + 1)}{4b(x - 1)}\ \dfrac{x + 1}{2(x - 1)}, b \neq 0, x \neq 1$

5. $\dfrac{12x}{8(x + 1)}\ \dfrac{3x}{2(x + 1)}, x \neq -1$

6. $\dfrac{4a(x + 1)}{2a}\ 2(x + 1), a \neq 0$

7. $\dfrac{x^2 + 5x + 6}{x + 3}\ x + 2, x \neq -3$

8. $\dfrac{x^2 - 2x - 3}{x^2 - 1}\ \dfrac{x - 3}{x - 1}, x \neq -1, 1$

9. $\dfrac{x + 8}{x^2 + 11x + 24}\ \dfrac{1}{x + 3}, x \neq -8, -3$

10. $\dfrac{3a^5b^2}{18a^5b^3}\ \dfrac{1}{6b}, a \neq 0, b \neq 0$

11. $\dfrac{6x^2 + 7x + 2}{4x^2 - 1}\ \dfrac{3x + 2}{2x - 1}, x \neq -\dfrac{1}{2}, \dfrac{1}{2}$

12. $\dfrac{4x - 4}{7x - 7}\ \dfrac{4}{7}, x \neq 1$

13. $\dfrac{x + 1}{x^3 - x}\ \dfrac{1}{x(x - 1)}, x \neq -1, 0, 1$

14. $\dfrac{6x - 30}{x^2 - 7x + 10}\ \dfrac{6}{x - 2}, x \neq 2, 5$

Study Guide

Multiplying Rational Expressions

To multiply rational expressions, you multiply the numerators and multiply the denominators. Then simplify.

Multiplying Rational Expressions
For all rational numbers $\frac{a}{b}$ and $\frac{c}{d}$, where $b \neq 0$ and $d \neq 0$, $$\frac{a}{b} \cdot \frac{c}{d} = \frac{ac}{bd}.$$

Example 1: Find $\dfrac{2c^2d}{5ab^2} \cdot \dfrac{a^2b}{3cd}$. Assume that no denominator has a value of 0.

$$\frac{2c^2d}{5ab^2} \cdot \frac{a^2b}{3cd} = \frac{2c^2d \cdot a^2b}{5ab^2 \cdot 3cd}$$

$$= \frac{2a^2bc^2d}{15ab^2cd}$$

$$= \frac{2ac}{15b}$$

You can often find products of rational expressions by factoring.

Example 2: Find $\dfrac{y^3 - 4y}{y^2 - 4y + 4} \cdot \dfrac{y^2 + 3y - 10}{y}$. Assume that no denominator has a value of 0.

$$\frac{y^3 - 4y}{y^2 - 4y + 4} \cdot \frac{y^2 + 3y - 10}{y} = \frac{\overset{1}{\cancel{y}}(\overset{1}{\cancel{y-2}})(y+2)}{(\underset{1}{\cancel{y-2}})(\underset{1}{\cancel{y-2}})} \cdot \frac{(y+5)(\overset{1}{\cancel{y-2}})}{\underset{1}{\cancel{y}}}$$

$$= (y+2)(y+5)$$

Find each product. Assume that no denominator has a value of 0.

1. $\dfrac{mn^2}{3} \cdot \dfrac{4}{mn}$

2. $\dfrac{x+4}{x-4} \cdot \dfrac{1}{x+4}$

3. $\dfrac{m-5}{8} \cdot \dfrac{16}{m-5}$

4. $\dfrac{5x+5y}{3x^2} \cdot \dfrac{xy^3}{15x+15y}$

5. $\dfrac{8x^3y}{3x^2} \cdot \dfrac{9y}{4x^2}$

6. $\dfrac{a-5}{a+2} \cdot \dfrac{a^2-4}{a-5}$

7. $\dfrac{16x+8}{x^2-2x+1} \cdot \dfrac{x-1}{2x+2}$

8. $\dfrac{x^2-16}{2x+8} \cdot \dfrac{x+4}{x^2+8x+16}$

9. $\dfrac{v^2-4v-21}{3v^2+6v} \cdot \dfrac{v^2+8v}{v^2+11v+24}$

10. $\dfrac{2b-2c}{10bc} \cdot \dfrac{5bc}{3b-3c}$

11. $\dfrac{3p-3q}{10pq} \cdot \dfrac{20p^2q^2}{p^2-q^2}$

12. $\dfrac{a^2+7a+12}{a^2+2a-8} \cdot \dfrac{a^2+3a-10}{a^2+2a-8}$

NAME_____ DATE _____

Study Guide

Multiplying Rational Expressions

To multiply rational expressions, you multiply the numerators and multiply the denominators. Then simplify.

Multiplying Rational Expressions
For all rational numbers $\frac{a}{b}$ and $\frac{c}{d}$, where $b \neq 0$ and $d \neq 0$, $$\frac{a}{b} \cdot \frac{c}{d} = \frac{ac}{bd}.$$

Example 1: Find $\dfrac{2c^2d}{5ab^2} \cdot \dfrac{a^2b}{3cd}$. Assume that no denominator has a value of 0.

$$\frac{2c^2d}{5ab^2} \cdot \frac{a^2b}{3cd} = \frac{2c^2d \cdot a^2b}{5ab^2 \cdot 3cd}$$

$$= \frac{2a^2bc^2d}{15ab^2cd}$$

$$= \frac{2ac}{15b}$$

You can often find products of rational expressions by factoring.

Example 2: Find $\dfrac{y^3 - 4y}{y^2 - 4y + 4} \cdot \dfrac{y^2 + 3y - 10}{y}$. Assume that no denominator has a value of 0.

$$\frac{y^3 - 4y}{y^2 - 4y + 4} \cdot \frac{y^2 + 3y - 10}{y} = \frac{\overset{1}{\cancel{y}}(\overset{1}{\cancel{y-2}})(y+2)}{(\underset{1}{\cancel{y-2}})(\underset{1}{\cancel{y-2}})} \cdot \frac{(y+5)(\overset{1}{\cancel{y-2}})}{\underset{1}{\cancel{y}}}$$

$$= (y+2)(y+5)$$

Find each product. Assume that no denominator has a value of 0.

1. $\dfrac{mn^2}{3} \cdot \dfrac{4}{mn}$ $\dfrac{4n}{3}$

2. $\dfrac{x+4}{x-4} \cdot \dfrac{1}{x+4}$ $\dfrac{1}{x-4}$

3. $\dfrac{m-5}{8} \cdot \dfrac{16}{m-5}$ **2**

4. $\dfrac{5x+5y}{3x^2} \cdot \dfrac{xy^3}{15x+15y}$ $\dfrac{y^3}{9x}$

5. $\dfrac{8x^3y}{3x^2} \cdot \dfrac{9y}{4x^2}$ $\dfrac{6y^2}{x}$

6. $\dfrac{a-5}{a+2} \cdot \dfrac{a^2-4}{a-5}$ **a − 2**

7. $\dfrac{16x+8}{x^2-2x+1} \cdot \dfrac{x-1}{2x+2}$ $\dfrac{4(2x+1)}{x^2-1}$**, or** $\dfrac{8x+4}{x^2-1}$

8. $\dfrac{x^2-16}{2x+8} \cdot \dfrac{x+4}{x^2+8x+16}$ $\dfrac{x-4}{2(x+4)}$

9. $\dfrac{v^2-4v-21}{3v^2+6v} \cdot \dfrac{v^2+8v}{v^2+11v+24}$ $\dfrac{v-7}{3(v+2)}$**, or** $\dfrac{v-7}{3v+6}$

10. $\dfrac{2b-2c}{10bc} \cdot \dfrac{5bc}{3b-3c}$ $\dfrac{1}{3}$

11. $\dfrac{3p-3q}{10pq} \cdot \dfrac{20p^2q^2}{p^2-q^2}$ $\dfrac{6pq}{p+q}$

12. $\dfrac{a^2+7a+12}{a^2+2a-8} \cdot \dfrac{a^2+3a-10}{a^2+2a-8}$ $\dfrac{(a+3)(a+5)}{(a-2)(a+4)}$**, or** $\dfrac{a^2+8a+15}{a^2+2a-8}$

 Algebra 1

Study Guide

Dividing Rational Expressions

You should recall that two numbers whose product is 1 are called **multiplicative inverses** or **reciprocals**. To find the quotient of two rational expressions, you multiply the first rational expression by the reciprocal of the second rational expression.

Dividing Rational Expressions
For all rational numbers $\frac{a}{b}$ and $\frac{c}{d}$, where $b \neq 0$, $c \neq 0$ and $d \neq 0$, $$\frac{a}{b} \div \frac{c}{d} = \frac{a}{b} \cdot \frac{d}{c}.$$

Example 1: Find $\frac{2}{x} \div \frac{z}{y}$.

$$\frac{2}{x} \div \frac{z}{y} = \frac{2}{x} \cdot \frac{y}{z}$$

$$= \frac{2y}{xz}$$

Example 2: Find $\frac{x^2 + 6x - 27}{x^2 + 11x + 18} \div \frac{x - 3}{x^2 + x - 2}$.

$$\frac{x^2 + 6x - 27}{x^2 + 11x + 18} \div \frac{x - 3}{x^2 + x - 2} = \frac{x^2 + 6x - 27}{x^2 + 11x + 18} \cdot \frac{x^2 + x - 2}{x - 3}$$

$$= \frac{\overset{1}{\cancel{(x + 9)}}\overset{1}{\cancel{(x - 3)}}}{\underset{1}{\cancel{(x + 9)}}\underset{1}{\cancel{(x + 2)}}} \cdot \frac{\overset{1}{\cancel{(x + 2)}}(x - 1)}{\underset{1}{\cancel{x - 3}}}$$

$$= x - 1$$

Find each quotient. Assume that no denominator has a value of 0.

1. $\frac{5}{6} \div \frac{1}{6}$

2. $1 \div \frac{1}{3}$

3. $\frac{n}{4} \div \frac{n}{m}$

4. $\frac{6}{11} \div \frac{12}{7x}$

5. $\frac{x}{y} \div \frac{2}{y}$

6. $\frac{a + b}{a - b} \div (a^2 + 2ab + b^2)$

7. $\frac{3x^2y}{8} \div 6xy$

8. $\frac{y^2 - 36}{y^2 - 49} \div \frac{y + 6}{y + 7}$

9. $\frac{x^2 - 5x + 6}{5} \div \frac{x - 3}{15}$

10. $\frac{49 - m^2}{m} \div \frac{m^2 - 13m + 42}{3m^2}$

11. $\frac{3a^3 - 27a}{2a^2 + 13a - 7} \div \frac{9a^2}{4a^2 - 1}$

12. $\frac{p^2 - 5p + 6}{p^2 + 3p} \div \frac{3 - p}{4p + 12}$

NAME_____ DATE _____

Study Guide

Dividing Rational Expressions

You should recall that two numbers whose product is 1 are called **multiplicative inverses** or **reciprocals.** To find the quotient of two rational expressions, you multiply the first rational expression by the reciprocal of the second rational expression.

Dividing Rational Expressions
For all rational numbers $\frac{a}{b}$ and $\frac{c}{d}$, where $b \neq 0$, $c \neq 0$ and $d \neq 0$, $$\frac{a}{b} \div \frac{c}{d} = \frac{a}{b} \cdot \frac{d}{c}.$$

Example 1: Find $\frac{2}{x} \div \frac{z}{y}$.

$$\frac{2}{x} \div \frac{z}{y} = \frac{2}{x} \cdot \frac{y}{z}$$
$$= \frac{2y}{xz}$$

Example 2: Find $\frac{x^2 + 6x - 27}{x^2 + 11x + 18} \div \frac{x - 3}{x^2 + x - 2}$.

$$\frac{x^2 + 6x - 27}{x^2 + 11x + 18} \div \frac{x - 3}{x^2 + x - 2} = \frac{x^2 + 6x - 27}{x^2 + 11x + 18} \cdot \frac{x^2 + x - 2}{x - 3}$$

$$= \frac{\cancel{(x+9)}\cancel{(x-3)}}{\cancel{(x+9)}(x+2)} \cdot \frac{(x+2)(x-1)}{\cancel{x-3}}$$

$$= x - 1$$

Find each quotient. Assume that no denominator has a value of 0.

1. $\frac{5}{6} \div \frac{1}{6}$ **5**

2. $1 \div \frac{1}{3}$ **3**

3. $\frac{n}{4} \div \frac{n}{m}$ $\frac{m}{4}$

4. $\frac{6}{11} \div \frac{12}{7x}$ $\frac{7x}{22}$

5. $\frac{x}{y} \div \frac{2}{y}$ $\frac{x}{2}$

6. $\frac{a + b}{a - b} \div (a^2 + 2ab + b^2)$ $\frac{1}{a^2 - b^2}$

7. $\frac{3x^2y}{8} \div 6xy$ $\frac{x}{16}$

8. $\frac{y^2 - 36}{y^2 - 49} \div \frac{y + 6}{y + 7}$ $\frac{y - 6}{y - 7}$

9. $\frac{x^2 - 5x + 6}{5} \div \frac{x - 3}{15}$ $3(x - 2)$

10. $\frac{49 - m^2}{m} \div \frac{m^2 - 13m + 42}{3m^2}$ $\frac{-3m(m + 7)}{m - 6}$, or $\frac{-3m^2 - 21m}{m - 6}$

11. $\frac{3a^3 - 27a}{2a^2 + 13a - 7} \div \frac{9a^2}{4a^2 - 1}$ $\frac{(a^2 - 9)(2a + 1)}{3a(a + 7)}$, or $\frac{2a^3 + a^2 - 18a - 9}{3a^2 + 21a}$

12. $\frac{p^2 - 5p + 6}{p^2 + 3p} \div \frac{3 - p}{4p + 12}$ $\frac{4(2 - p)}{p}$, or $\frac{8 - 4p}{p}$

Study Guide

Dividing Polynomials

To divide a polynomial by a polynomial, you can use a long division process similar to that used for numbers.

Example: Find $(x^2 + 7x + 12) \div (x + 3)$.

Step 1 To find the first term of the quotient, divide the first term of the dividend (x^2) by the first term of the divisor (x).

$$
\begin{array}{r}
x \\
x + 3 \overline{) x^2 + 7x + 12} \\
\underline{x^2 + 3x} \\
4x
\end{array}
$$

Step 2 To find the next term of the quotient, divide the first term of the partial dividend ($4x + 12$) by the first term of the divisor (x).

$$
\begin{array}{r}
x + 4 \\
x + 3 \overline{) x^2 + 7x + 12} \\
\underline{x^2 + 3x} \\
4x + 12 \\
\underline{4x + 12} \\
0
\end{array}
$$

Therefore, $x^2 + 7x + 12$ divided by $x + 3$ is $x + 4$. This means that $(x + 3)(x + 4) = x^2 + 7x + 12$.

If the divisor is not a factor of the dividend, there will be a nonzero remainder. When there is a nonzero remainder, the quotient can be expressed as follows:

$$\text{quotient} = \text{partial quotient} + \frac{\text{remainder}}{\text{divisor}}$$

Find each quotient.

1. $(b^2 - 5b + 6) \div (b - 2)$

2. $(x^2 - x - 6) \div (x - 3)$

3. $(3x^3 + 15x^2 - 21x) \div 3x$

4. $\dfrac{-6x - 9 + 8x^2}{4x + 3}$

5. $\dfrac{x^3 + 1}{x - 2}$

6. $\dfrac{6x^2 + 7x + 5}{2x + 5}$

7. $\dfrac{6x^3 + 11x^2 + 4x + 35}{2x + 5}$

8. $\dfrac{8x^3 + 27}{2x + 3}$

9. $\dfrac{15x^2 + 13x + 5}{5x + 1}$

Dividing Polynomials

To divide a polynomial by a polynomial, you can use a long
division process similar to that used for numbers.

Example: Find $(x^2 + 7x + 12) \div (x + 3)$.

Step 1 To find the first term of the
quotient, divide the first term of the
dividend (x^2) by the first term of the
divisor (x).

$$
\begin{array}{r}
x \\
x + 3 \overline{)x^2 + 7x + 12} \\
\underline{x^2 + 3x} \\
4x
\end{array}
$$

Step 2 To find the next term of the
quotient, divide the first term of the
partial dividend $(4x + 12)$ by the first
term of the divisor (x).

$$
\begin{array}{r}
x + 4 \\
x + 3 \overline{)x^2 + 7x + 12} \\
\underline{x^2 + 3x} \\
4x + 12 \\
\underline{4x + 12} \\
0
\end{array}
$$

Therefore, $x^2 + 7x + 12$ divided by $x + 3$ is $x + 4$. This means
that $(x + 3)(x + 4) = x^2 + 7x + 12$.

If the divisor is not a factor of the dividend, there will be a
nonzero remainder. When there is a nonzero remainder, the
quotient can be expressed as follows:

$$\text{quotient} = \text{partial quotient} + \frac{\text{remainder}}{\text{divisor}}$$

Find each quotient.

1. $(b^2 - 5b + 6) \div (b - 2)$
  $b - 3$

2. $(x^2 - x - 6) \div (x - 3)$
  $x + 2$

3. $(3x^3 + 15x^2 - 21x) \div 3x$
  $x^2 + 5x - 7$

4. $\dfrac{-6x - 9 + 8x^2}{4x + 3}$
  $2x - 3$

5. $\dfrac{x^3 + 1}{x - 2}$
  $x^2 + 2x + 4 + \dfrac{9}{x - 2}$

6. $\dfrac{6x^2 + 7x + 5}{2x + 5}$
  $3x - 4 + \dfrac{25}{2x + 5}$

7. $\dfrac{6x^3 + 11x^2 + 4x + 35}{2x + 5}$
  $3x^2 - 2x + 7$

8. $\dfrac{8x^3 + 27}{2x + 3}$ $4x^2 - 6x + 9$

9. $\dfrac{15x^2 + 13x + 5}{5x + 1}$
  $3x + 2 + \dfrac{3}{5x + 1}$

12-5

Study Guide

Rational Expressions with Like Denominators

To add or subtract rational expressions with *like* denominators, you simply add or subtract the numerators, then write the sum or difference over the common denominator. If possible, you simplify the resulting rational expression.

Adding or Subtracting Rational Expressions
For all rational numbers $\frac{a}{b}$ and $\frac{c}{b}$, where $b \neq 0$,
$\frac{a}{b} + \frac{c}{b} = \frac{a+c}{b}$ and $\frac{a}{b} - \frac{c}{b} = \frac{a-c}{b}$.

Example 1: Find $\frac{x}{2} - \frac{5-x}{2}$.

$$\frac{x}{2} - \frac{5-x}{2} = \frac{x - (5-x)}{2}$$
$$= \frac{x - 5 + x}{2}$$
$$= \frac{2x - 5}{2}$$

Example 2: Find $\frac{-y^3}{y+z} + \frac{yz^2}{y+z}$.

$$\frac{-y^3}{y+z} + \frac{yz^2}{y+z} = \frac{-y^3 + yz^2}{y+z}$$
$$= \frac{y(z + y)(z - y)}{(z + y)}$$
$$= y(z - y)$$

Find each sum or difference. Express in simplest form.

1. $\frac{3}{a} + \frac{4}{a}$

2. $\frac{5x}{9} - \frac{x}{9}$

3. $\frac{y+2}{2y} + \frac{y+4}{2y}$

4. $\frac{x}{x^2 - 1} - \frac{1}{x^2 - 1}$

5. $\frac{x^2 + 2x}{x - 4} - \frac{x^2 + 8}{x - 4}$

6. $\frac{x^2 - x}{6x^2 - x} + \frac{x^2 - 2x}{6x^2 - x}$

7. $\frac{4x - 4y}{4x + 4y} - \frac{4x}{4x + 4y}$

8. $\frac{2x}{2x^2 + 3x - 5} + \frac{5}{2x^2 + 3x - 5}$

9. $\frac{8t}{w + 6} - \frac{3t}{w + 6}$

10. $\frac{c^2}{c + 2} - \frac{4}{c + 2}$

11. $\frac{11x}{15y} - \frac{-x}{15y}$

12. $\frac{x^2 + x}{x - 2} - \frac{6}{x - 2}$

13. $\frac{7n + 1}{3n + 1} - \frac{4n}{3n + 1}$

14. $\frac{3x + 2}{x + 2} + \frac{x + 6}{x + 2}$

15. $\frac{5a}{3b^2} + \frac{10a}{3b^2}$

Algebra 1

NAME_____ DATE _____

Study Guide

Rational Expressions with Like Denominators

To add or subtract rational expressions with *like* denominators, you simply add or subtract the numerators, then write the sum or difference over the common denominator. If possible, you simplify the resulting rational expression.

Adding or Subtracting Rational Expressions
For all rational numbers $\frac{a}{b}$ and $\frac{c}{b}$, where $b \neq 0$,
$\frac{a}{b} + \frac{c}{b} = \frac{a+c}{b}$ and $\frac{a}{b} - \frac{c}{b} = \frac{a-c}{b}$.

Example 1: Find $\frac{x}{2} - \frac{5-x}{2}$.

$$\frac{x}{2} - \frac{5-x}{2} = \frac{x-(5-x)}{2}$$
$$= \frac{x-5+x}{2}$$
$$= \frac{2x-5}{2}$$

Example 2: Find $\frac{-y^3}{y+z} + \frac{yz^2}{y+z}$.

$$\frac{-y^3}{y+z} + \frac{yz^2}{y+z} = \frac{-y^3+yz^2}{y+z}$$
$$= \frac{y\cancel{(z+y)}(z-y)}{\cancel{(z+y)}}$$
$$= y(z-y)$$

Find each sum or difference. Express in simplest form.

1. $\frac{3}{a} + \frac{4}{a}$ $\frac{7}{a}$

2. $\frac{5x}{9} - \frac{x}{9}$ $\frac{4x}{9}$

3. $\frac{y+2}{2y} + \frac{y+4}{2y}$ $\frac{y+3}{y}$

4. $\frac{x}{x^2-1} - \frac{1}{x^2-1}$

$\frac{1}{x+1}$

5. $\frac{x^2+2x}{x-4} - \frac{x^2+8}{x-4}$ 2

6. $\frac{x^2-x}{6x^2-x} + \frac{x^2-2x}{6x^2-x}$

$\frac{2x-3}{6x-1}$

7. $\frac{4x-4y}{4x+4y} - \frac{4x}{4x+4y}$

$\frac{-y}{x+y}$

8. $\frac{2x}{2x^2+3x-5} + \frac{5}{2x^2+3x-5}$

$\frac{1}{x-1}$

9. $\frac{8t}{w+6} - \frac{3t}{w+6}$

$\frac{5t}{w+6}$

10. $\frac{c^2}{c+2} - \frac{4}{c+2}$

$c-2$

11. $\frac{11x}{15y} - \frac{-x}{15y}$ $\frac{4x}{5y}$

12. $\frac{x^2+x}{x-2} - \frac{6}{x-2}$

$x+3$

13. $\frac{7n+1}{3n+1} - \frac{4n}{3n+1}$ 1

14. $\frac{3x+2}{x+2} + \frac{x+6}{x+2}$ 4

15. $\frac{5a}{3b^2} + \frac{10a}{3b^2}$ $\frac{5a}{b^2}$

Algebra 1

Study Guide

Rational Expressions with Unlike Denominators

When you add or subtract rational expressions with *unlike* denominators, you must first rename the rational expressions so the denominators are alike. Any common denominator could be used. However, the computation is easier if the **least common denominator** (LCD) is used. The least common denominator is the **least common multiple** (LCM) of the denominators.

Example: Find $\dfrac{1}{2x^2 + 6x} + \dfrac{3}{x^2}$.

$$\frac{1}{2x^2 + 6x} + \frac{3}{x^2} = \frac{1}{2x(x + 3)} + \frac{3}{x^2}$$

$$= \frac{1}{2x(x + 3)} \cdot \frac{x}{x} + \frac{3}{x^2} \cdot \frac{2(x + 3)}{2(x + 3)}$$

$$= \frac{x + 3(2)(x + 3)}{2x^2(x + 3)}$$

$$= \frac{x + 6x + 18}{2x^2(x + 3)}$$

$$= \frac{7x + 18}{2x^2(x + 3)}$$

Find each sum or difference.

1. $\dfrac{1}{x} + \dfrac{7}{3x}$

2. $\dfrac{1}{6x} + \dfrac{3}{8}$

3. $\dfrac{x}{x - 3} - \dfrac{3}{x + 3}$

4. $\dfrac{4}{h + 1} + \dfrac{2}{h + 2}$

5. $\dfrac{x}{6x + 6} - \dfrac{1}{x + 1}$

6. $\dfrac{4x}{6x - 2y} + \dfrac{3y}{9x - 3y}$

7. $\dfrac{y + 2}{y^2 + 5y + 6} + \dfrac{2 - y}{y^2 + y - 6}$

8. $\dfrac{x}{x - 7} - \dfrac{x + 3}{x^2 - 4x - 21}$

9. $\dfrac{a - 6b}{2a^2 - 5ab + 2b^2} - \dfrac{7}{a - 2b}$

10. $\dfrac{m}{1 - 2m} + \dfrac{4}{2m - 1}$

11. $\dfrac{7d + 4}{3d + 9} - \dfrac{2d}{d + 3}$

12. $\dfrac{q}{q^2 - 16} + \dfrac{q + 1}{q^2 + 5q + 4}$

Rational Expressions with Unlike Denominators

When you add or subtract rational expressions with *unlike* denominators, you must first rename the rational expressions so the denominators are alike. Any common denominator could be used. However, the computation is easier if the **least common denominator** (LCD) is used. The least common denominator is the **least common multiple** (LCM) of the denominators.

Example: Find $\dfrac{1}{2x^2 + 6x} + \dfrac{3}{x^2}$.

$$\dfrac{1}{2x^2 + 6x} + \dfrac{3}{x^2} = \dfrac{1}{2x(x + 3)} + \dfrac{3}{x^2}$$

$$= \dfrac{1}{2x(x + 3)} \cdot \dfrac{x}{x} + \dfrac{3}{x^2} \cdot \dfrac{2(x + 3)}{2(x + 3)}$$

$$= \dfrac{x + 3(2)(x + 3)}{2x^2(x + 3)}$$

$$= \dfrac{x + 6x + 18}{2x^2(x + 3)}$$

$$= \dfrac{7x + 18}{2x^2(x + 3)}$$

Find each sum or difference.

1. $\dfrac{1}{x} + \dfrac{7}{3x}$ $\dfrac{10}{3x}$

2. $\dfrac{1}{6x} + \dfrac{3}{8}$ $\dfrac{4 + 9x}{24x}$

3. $\dfrac{x}{x - 3} - \dfrac{3}{x + 3}$ $\dfrac{x^2 + 9}{x^2 - 9}$

4. $\dfrac{4}{h + 1} + \dfrac{2}{h + 2}$ $\dfrac{6h + 10}{(h + 1)(h + 2)}$, **or** $\dfrac{6h + 10}{h^2 + 3h + 2}$

5. $\dfrac{x}{6x + 6} - \dfrac{1}{x + 1}$ $\dfrac{x - 6}{6(x + 1)}$, **or** $\dfrac{x - 6}{6x + 6}$

6. $\dfrac{4x}{6x - 2y} + \dfrac{3y}{9x - 3y}$ $\dfrac{2x + y}{3x - y}$

7. $\dfrac{y + 2}{y^2 + 5y + 6} + \dfrac{2 - y}{y^2 + y - 6}$ 0

8. $\dfrac{x}{x - 7} - \dfrac{x + 3}{x^2 - 4x - 21}$ $\dfrac{x - 1}{x - 7}$

9. $\dfrac{a - 6b}{2a^2 - 5ab + 2b^2} - \dfrac{7}{a - 2b}$ $\dfrac{-13a + b}{(2a - b)(a - 2b)}$, **or** $\dfrac{-13a + b}{2a^2 - 5ab + 2b^2}$

10. $\dfrac{m}{1 - 2m} + \dfrac{4}{2m - 1}$ $\dfrac{4 - m}{2m - 1}$

11. $\dfrac{7d + 4}{3d + 9} - \dfrac{2d}{d + 3}$ $\dfrac{d + 4}{3(d + 3)}$, **or** $\dfrac{d + 4}{3d + 9}$

12. $\dfrac{q}{q^2 - 16} + \dfrac{q + 1}{q^2 + 5q + 4}$ $\dfrac{2(q - 2)}{(q - 4)(q + 4)}$, **or** $\dfrac{2q - 4}{q^2 - 16}$

12-7

Study Guide

Mixed Expressions and Complex Fractions

Algebraic expressions such as $a + \dfrac{b}{c}$ and $5 + \dfrac{x + y}{x + 3}$ are called **mixed expressions.** Changing mixed expressions to improper fractions is similar to changing mixed numbers to improper fractions.

If a fraction has one or more fractions in the numerator or denominator, it is called a **complex fraction.**

Simplifying Complex Fractions
Any complex fraction $\dfrac{\frac{a}{b}}{\frac{c}{d}}$, where $b \neq 0$, $c \neq 0$, and $d \neq 0$, may be expressed as $\dfrac{a}{b} \cdot \dfrac{d}{c}$, or $\dfrac{ad}{bc}$.

Example: Simplify $\dfrac{2 + \frac{4}{a}}{\frac{a+2}{3}}$.

$$\dfrac{2 + \frac{4}{a}}{\frac{a+2}{3}} = \dfrac{\frac{2a}{a} + \frac{4}{a}}{\frac{a+2}{3}}$$

$$= \dfrac{\frac{2a+4}{a}}{\frac{a+2}{3}}$$

$$= \dfrac{2a+4}{a} \cdot \dfrac{3}{a+2}$$

$$= \dfrac{2(a+2)}{a} \cdot \dfrac{3}{a+2}$$

$$= \dfrac{6}{a}$$

Simplify.

1. $10 + \dfrac{60}{x+5}$

2. $12 + \dfrac{x-y}{x+y}$

3. $4 - \dfrac{4}{2x+1}$

4. $\dfrac{2\frac{2}{5}}{3\frac{3}{4}}$

5. $\dfrac{\frac{3}{x}}{\frac{4}{y}}$

6. $\dfrac{\frac{3}{y+2} - \frac{2}{y-2}}{\frac{1}{y+2} - \frac{2}{y-2}}$

7. $\dfrac{1 - \frac{1}{x}}{1 - \frac{1}{x^2}}$

8. $\dfrac{\frac{1}{x-3}}{\frac{2}{x^2-9}}$

9. $\dfrac{\frac{x^2-25}{y}}{x^3-5x^2}$

Algebra 1

Study Guide

Mixed Expressions and Complex Fractions

Algebraic expressions such as $a + \dfrac{b}{c}$ and $5 + \dfrac{x+y}{x+3}$ are called **mixed expressions**. Changing mixed expressions to improper fractions is similar to changing mixed numbers to improper fractions.

If a fraction has one or more fractions in the numerator or denominator, it is called a **complex fraction.**

Example: Simplify $\dfrac{2 + \frac{4}{a}}{\frac{a+2}{3}}$.

$$\frac{2 + \frac{4}{a}}{\frac{a+2}{3}} = \frac{\frac{2a}{a} + \frac{4}{a}}{\frac{a+2}{3}}$$

$$= \frac{\frac{2a+4}{a}}{\frac{a+2}{3}}$$

$$= \frac{2a+4}{a} \cdot \frac{3}{a+2}$$

$$= \frac{2(a+2)}{a} \cdot \frac{3}{a+2}$$

$$= \frac{6}{a}$$

Simplifying Complex Fractions
Any complex fraction $\dfrac{\frac{a}{b}}{\frac{c}{d}}$, where $b \neq 0$, $c \neq 0$, and $d \neq 0$, may be expressed as $\dfrac{a}{b} \cdot \dfrac{d}{c}$, or $\dfrac{ad}{bc}$.

Simplify.

1. $10 + \dfrac{60}{x+5}$

$\dfrac{10x+110}{x+5}$

2. $12 + \dfrac{x-y}{x+y}$

$\dfrac{13x+11y}{x+y}$

3. $4 - \dfrac{4}{2x+1}$

$\dfrac{8x}{2x+1}$

4. $\dfrac{2\frac{2}{5}}{3\frac{3}{4}}$ $\dfrac{16}{25}$

5. $\dfrac{\frac{3}{x}}{\frac{4}{y}}$ $\dfrac{3y}{4x}$

6. $\dfrac{\frac{3}{y+2} - \frac{2}{y-2}}{\frac{1}{y+2} - \frac{2}{y-2}}$ $\dfrac{y-10}{-y-6}$

7. $\dfrac{1 - \frac{1}{x}}{1 - \frac{1}{x^2}}$ $\dfrac{x}{x+1}$

8. $\dfrac{\frac{1}{x-3}}{\frac{2}{x^2-9}}$ $\dfrac{x+3}{2}$

9. $\dfrac{\frac{x^2-25}{y}}{x^3-5x^2}$ $\dfrac{x+5}{x^2y}$

Study Guide

Solving Rational Equations

To solve equations containing fractions, eliminate the fractions by multiplying each side of the equation by a common denominator.

Example 1: Solve $\dfrac{x-3}{3} + \dfrac{x}{2} = 4$.

$$6\left(\dfrac{x-3}{3} + \dfrac{x}{2}\right) = 6 \cdot 4$$
$$2(x-3) + 3(x) = 24$$
$$2x - 6 + 3x = 24$$
$$5x = 30$$
$$x = 6$$

Problems involving work can be solved by calculating the rate of work and the time spent working as shown below.

$$\text{(rate of working)} \cdot \text{(time)} = \text{(work done)}$$
$$r \quad\quad \cdot \quad t \quad = \quad w$$

Uniform motion problems can be solved by using a formula similar to the one used to solve work problems.

$$\text{(rate)} \cdot \text{(time)} = \text{(distance)}$$
$$r \quad \cdot \quad t \quad = \quad d$$

Example 2: Marla can paint Percy's kitchen in 3 hours. Percy can paint it in 2 hours. Working together, how long will it take Marla and Percy to paint the kitchen?

$$\dfrac{t}{3} + \dfrac{t}{2} = 1$$
$$2t + 3t = 6$$
$$5t = 6$$
$$t = \dfrac{6}{5} \text{ or } 1\dfrac{1}{5} \text{ hours}$$

Together Marla and Percy can paint the kitchen in $1\dfrac{1}{5}$ hours, or 1 hour and 12 minutes.

Solve each equation.

1. $\dfrac{x-5}{5} + \dfrac{x}{4} = 8$

2. $\dfrac{4}{8y} - \dfrac{3y}{y-1} = -2$

3. $s - \dfrac{4}{s+3} = s + 3$

4. $\dfrac{m+4}{m} + \dfrac{m}{3} = \dfrac{m}{3}$

5. $\dfrac{q+4}{q-1} + \dfrac{q}{q+1} = 2$

6. $\dfrac{5-2x}{2} - \dfrac{4x+3}{6} = \dfrac{7x+2}{6}$

7. A motorboat went upstream at 15 mi/h and returned downstream at 20 mi/h. How far did the boat travel one way if the round trip took 3.5 hours?

8. It takes Kenesha 45 minutes to prepare 20 greeting cards. It takes Paula 30 minutes to prepare the same cards. Working together at this rate, how long will it take them to prepare the cards?

NAME_____ DATE _____

Study Guide

Student Edition
Pages 696–702

Solving Rational Equations

To solve equations containing fractions, eliminate the fractions by multiplying each side of the equation by a common denominator.

Example 1: Solve $\dfrac{x-3}{3} + \dfrac{x}{2} = 4$.

$$6\left(\dfrac{x-3}{3} + \dfrac{x}{2}\right) = 6 \cdot 4$$
$$2(x-3) + 3(x) = 24$$
$$2x - 6 + 3x = 24$$
$$5x = 30$$
$$x = 6$$

Problems involving work can be solved by calculating the rate of work and the time spent working as shown below.

$$\text{(rate of working)} \cdot \text{(time)} = \text{(work done)}$$
$$r \quad \cdot \quad t \quad = \quad w$$

Uniform motion problems can be solved by using a formula similar to the one used to solve work problems.

$$\text{(rate)} \cdot \text{(time)} = \text{(distance)}$$
$$r \quad \cdot \quad t \quad = \quad d$$

Example 2: Marla can paint Percy's kitchen in 3 hours. Percy can paint it in 2 hours. Working together, how long will it take Marla and Percy to paint the kitchen?

$$\dfrac{t}{3} + \dfrac{t}{2} = 1$$
$$2t + 3t = 6$$
$$5t = 6$$
$$t = \dfrac{6}{5} \text{ or } 1\dfrac{1}{5} \text{ hours}$$

Together Marla and Percy can paint the kitchen in $1\dfrac{1}{5}$ hours, or 1 hour and 12 minutes.

Solve each equation.

1. $\dfrac{x-5}{5} + \dfrac{x}{4} = 8$

   20

2. $\dfrac{4}{8y} - \dfrac{3y}{y-1} = -2$

   -1 or $-\dfrac{1}{2}$

3. $s - \dfrac{4}{s+3} = s + 3$

   $-4\dfrac{1}{3}$

4. $\dfrac{m+4}{m} + \dfrac{m}{3} = \dfrac{m}{3}$

   -4

5. $\dfrac{q+4}{q-1} + \dfrac{q}{q+1} = 2$

   $-\dfrac{3}{2}$

6. $\dfrac{5-2x}{2} - \dfrac{4x+3}{6} = \dfrac{7x+2}{6}$

   $\dfrac{10}{17}$

7. A motorboat went upstream at 15 mi/h and returned downstream at 20 mi/h. How far did the boat travel one way if the round trip took 3.5 hours? **30 miles**

8. It takes Kenesha 45 minutes to prepare 20 greeting cards. It takes Paula 30 minutes to prepare the same cards. Working together at this rate, how long will it take them to prepare the cards? **18 minutes**

Study Guide

Integration: Geometry
The Pythagorean Theorem

The side opposite the right angle in a right triangle is called the **hypotenuse.** This side is always the longest side of a right triangle. The other two sides are called the **legs** of the triangle. To find the length of any side of a right triangle, given the lengths of the other two sides, you can use the *Pythagorean theorem.*

The Pythagorean Theorem
In a right triangle, if a and b are the measures of the legs and c is the measure of the hypotenuse, then $c^2 = a^2 + b^2$.

Example: Find the length of a leg of a right triangle if $a = 8$ and $c = 10$.

$$c^2 = a^2 + b^2$$
$$10^2 = 8^2 + b^2$$
$$100 = 64 + b^2$$
$$b^2 = 36$$
$$b = 6$$

The length of the leg is 6 units.

If c is the measure of the hypotenuse of a right triangle, find each missing measure. Round answers to the nearest hundredth.

1. $a = 10$, $b = 12$, $c = \underline{\ ?\ }$

2. $a = 9$, $b = 12$, $c = \underline{\ ?\ }$

3. $a = 12$, $b = \underline{\ ?\ }$, $c = 16$

4. $a = \underline{\ ?\ }$, $b = 6$, $c = 8$

5. $a = \sqrt{5}$, $b = \sqrt{10}$, $c = \underline{\ ?\ }$

6. $a = \underline{\ ?\ }$, $b = \sqrt{8}$, $c = \sqrt{18}$

For each problem, make a drawing. Then use an equation to solve the problem. Round answers to the nearest hundredth.

7. How long is a pipeline that runs diagonally across a square field 6 kilometers on a side?

8. A support wire on a television tower is 90 meters long and meets the ground 35 meters from the center of the base of the tower. What is the height of the tower?

NAME _____ DATE _____

Study Guide

Integration: Geometry
The Pythagorean Theorem

The side opposite the right angle in a right triangle is called the **hypotenuse.** This side is always the longest side of a right triangle. The other two sides are called the **legs** of the triangle. To find the length of any side of a right triangle, given the lengths of the other two sides, you can use the *Pythagorean theorem.*

The Pythagorean Theorem
In a right triangle, if a and b are the measures of the legs and c is the measure of the hypotenuse, then $c^2 = a^2 + b^2$.

Example: Find the length of a leg of a right triangle if $a = 8$ and $c = 10$.

$$c^2 = a^2 + b^2$$
$$10^2 = 8^2 + b^2$$
$$100 = 64 + b^2$$
$$b^2 = 36$$
$$b = 6$$

The length of the leg is 6 units.

If c is the measure of the hypotenuse of a right triangle, find each missing measure. Round answers to the nearest hundredth.

1. $a = 10$, $b = 12$, $c = \underline{\ ?\ }$
   15.62

2. $a = 9$, $b = 12$, $c = \underline{\ ?\ }$
   15

3. $a = 12$, $b = \underline{\ ?\ }$, $c = 16$
   10.58

4. $a = \underline{\ ?\ }$, $b = 6$, $c = 8$
   5.29

5. $a = \sqrt{5}$, $b = \sqrt{10}$, $c = \underline{\ ?\ }$ **3.87**

6. $a = \underline{\ ?\ }$, $b = \sqrt{8}$, $c = \sqrt{18}$ **3.16**

For each problem, make a drawing. Then use an equation to solve the problem. Round answers to the nearest hundredth.

7. How long is a pipeline that runs diagonally across a square field 6 kilometers on a side? **8.49 km**

8. A support wire on a television tower is 90 meters long and meets the ground 35 meters from the center of the base of the tower. What is the height of the tower? **89.92 m**

13-2

Study Guide

Simplifying Radical Expressions

The product property of square roots and prime factorization can be used to simplify irrational square roots. When you simplify radical expressions with variables, use absolute values to ensure nonnegative results.

Example 1: Simplify $\sqrt{180}$.

$$\begin{aligned}
\sqrt{180} &= \sqrt{2 \cdot 2 \cdot 3 \cdot 3 \cdot 5} \\
&= \sqrt{2 \cdot 2} \cdot \sqrt{3 \cdot 3} \cdot \sqrt{5} \\
&= 2 \cdot 3 \cdot \sqrt{5} \\
&= 6\sqrt{5}
\end{aligned}$$

Example 2: Simplify $\sqrt{100a^2}$.

$$\begin{aligned}
\sqrt{100a^2} &= \sqrt{100} \cdot \sqrt{a^2} \\
&= 10|a|
\end{aligned}$$

Use the quotient property of square roots and a method called **rationalizing the denominator** when simplifying radical expressions involving division. Study the example below.

Example 3: Simplify $\sqrt{\dfrac{56}{45}}$.

$$\begin{aligned}
\sqrt{\frac{56}{45}} &= \frac{\sqrt{56}}{\sqrt{45}} \\
&= \frac{2 \cdot \sqrt{14}}{3 \cdot \sqrt{5}} \\
&= \frac{2\sqrt{14}}{3\sqrt{5}} \cdot \frac{\sqrt{5}}{\sqrt{5}} = \frac{2\sqrt{70}}{15}
\end{aligned}$$

Simplify. Leave in radical form and use absolute value symbols when necessary.

1. $\sqrt{18}$ **2.** $\sqrt{68}$ **3.** $\sqrt{60}$ **4.** $\sqrt{75}$

5. $\sqrt{162}$ **6.** $\sqrt{4a^2}$ **7.** $\sqrt{9x^4}$ **8.** $\sqrt{300a^4}$

9. $\sqrt{128c^6}$ **10.** $\sqrt{5} \cdot \sqrt{10}$ **11.** $\sqrt{3x^2} \cdot 3\sqrt{3x^4}$ **12.** $4\sqrt{10} \cdot 3\sqrt{6}$

13. $\dfrac{\sqrt{9}}{\sqrt{18}}$ **14.** $\dfrac{\sqrt{8}}{\sqrt{24}}$ **15.** $\dfrac{\sqrt{x^6}}{\sqrt{y^4}}$ **16.** $\dfrac{\sqrt{100}}{\sqrt{121}}$

17. $\dfrac{\sqrt{75}}{\sqrt{3}}$ **18.** $\dfrac{8\sqrt{2}}{2\sqrt{8}}$ **19.** $\dfrac{\sqrt{4}}{3 - \sqrt{5}}$ **20.** $\dfrac{\sqrt{8}}{2\sqrt{7} + 4\sqrt{10}}$

Study Guide

Simplifying Radical Expressions

The product property of square roots and prime factorization
can be used to simplify irrational square roots. When you
simplify radical expressions with variables, use absolute values
to ensure nonnegative results.

Example 1: Simplify $\sqrt{180}$.

$$\begin{aligned}
\sqrt{180} &= \sqrt{2 \cdot 2 \cdot 3 \cdot 3 \cdot 5} \\
&= \sqrt{2 \cdot 2} \cdot \sqrt{3 \cdot 3} \cdot \sqrt{5} \\
&= 2 \cdot 3 \cdot \sqrt{5} \\
&= 6\sqrt{5}
\end{aligned}$$

Example 2: Simplify $\sqrt{100a^2}$.

$$\begin{aligned}
\sqrt{100a^2} &= \sqrt{100} \cdot \sqrt{a^2} \\
&= 10|a|
\end{aligned}$$

Use the quotient property of square roots and a method called
rationalizing the denominator when simplifying radical
expressions involving division. Study the example below.

Example 3: Simplify $\sqrt{\dfrac{56}{45}}$.

$$\begin{aligned}
\sqrt{\frac{56}{45}} &= \frac{\sqrt{56}}{\sqrt{45}} \\
&= \frac{2 \cdot \sqrt{14}}{3 \cdot \sqrt{5}} \\
&= \frac{2\sqrt{14}}{3\sqrt{5}} \cdot \frac{\sqrt{5}}{\sqrt{5}} = \frac{2\sqrt{70}}{15}
\end{aligned}$$

**Simplify. Leave in radical form and use absolute value
symbols when necessary.**

1. $\sqrt{18}$ $3\sqrt{2}$

2. $\sqrt{68}$ $2\sqrt{17}$

3. $\sqrt{60}$ $2\sqrt{15}$

4. $\sqrt{75}$ $5\sqrt{3}$

5. $\sqrt{162}$ $9\sqrt{2}$

6. $\sqrt{4a^2}$ $2|a|$

7. $\sqrt{9x^4}$ $3x^2$

8. $\sqrt{300a^4}$
$10a^2\sqrt{3}$

9. $\sqrt{128c^6}$
$8|c^3|\sqrt{2}$

10. $\sqrt{5} \cdot \sqrt{10}$
$5\sqrt{2}$

11. $\sqrt{3x^2} \cdot 3\sqrt{3x^4}$
$9|x^3|$

12. $4\sqrt{10} \cdot 3\sqrt{6}$
$24\sqrt{15}$

13. $\dfrac{\sqrt{9}}{\sqrt{18}}$ $\dfrac{\sqrt{2}}{2}$

14. $\dfrac{\sqrt{8}}{\sqrt{24}}$ $\dfrac{\sqrt{3}}{3}$

15. $\dfrac{\sqrt{x^6}}{\sqrt{y^4}}$ $\dfrac{|x^3|}{y^2}$

16. $\dfrac{\sqrt{100}}{\sqrt{121}}$ $\dfrac{10}{11}$

17. $\dfrac{\sqrt{75}}{\sqrt{3}}$ 5

18. $\dfrac{8\sqrt{2}}{2\sqrt{8}}$ 2

19. $\dfrac{\sqrt{4}}{3-\sqrt{5}}$ $\dfrac{3+\sqrt{5}}{2}$

20. $\dfrac{\sqrt{8}}{2\sqrt{7}+4\sqrt{10}}$
$\dfrac{4\sqrt{5}-\sqrt{14}}{33}$

Study Guide

Student Edition
Pages 727–731

Operations with Radical Expressions

When adding or subtracting radical expressions, use the distributive and commutative properties to simplify the expressions. If radical expressions are not in simplest form, first simplify.

Example 1: Simplify $10\sqrt{6} - 5\sqrt{3} + 6\sqrt{3} - 4\sqrt{6}$.

$$10\sqrt{6} - 5\sqrt{3} + 6\sqrt{3} - 4\sqrt{6} = 10\sqrt{6} - 4\sqrt{6} - 5\sqrt{3} + 6\sqrt{3}$$
$$= (10 - 4)\sqrt{6} + (-5 + 6)\sqrt{3}$$
$$= 6\sqrt{6} + \sqrt{3}$$

Example 2: Simplify $3\sqrt{12} + 5\sqrt{75}$.

$$3\sqrt{12} + 5\sqrt{75} = 3\sqrt{2^2 \cdot 3} + 5\sqrt{5^2 \cdot 3}$$
$$= 3 \cdot 2\sqrt{3} + 5 \cdot 5\sqrt{3}$$
$$= 6\sqrt{3} + 25\sqrt{3}$$
$$= (6 + 25)\sqrt{3}$$
$$= 31\sqrt{3}$$

Simplify. Then use a calculator to verify your answer.

1. $8 + 3\sqrt{2}$

2. $\sqrt{12} - \sqrt{27}$

3. $\sqrt{27} - 2\sqrt{3}$

4. $\sqrt{20} + 2\sqrt{5} - 3\sqrt{5}$

5. $-5\sqrt{6} + 8\sqrt{6}$

6. $\sqrt{200} - 3\sqrt{2}$

7. $\sqrt{54} + \sqrt{24}$

8. $\sqrt{18} - 3\sqrt{8} + \sqrt{50}$

9. $\sqrt{80} - \sqrt{20} + \sqrt{180}$

10. $2\sqrt{28} + 3\sqrt{63} - \sqrt{\dfrac{54}{3}}$

11. $\sqrt{12} + \sqrt{\dfrac{1}{3}}$

12. $\sqrt{54} - \sqrt{\dfrac{1}{6}} + \sqrt{24}$

Algebra 1

NAME_____ DATE _____

Study Guide

Operations with Radical Expressions

When adding or subtracting radical expressions, use the distributive and commutative properties to simplify the expressions. If radical expressions are not in simplest form, first simplify.

Example 1: Simplify $10\sqrt{6} - 5\sqrt{3} + 6\sqrt{3} - 4\sqrt{6}$.

$$10\sqrt{6} - 5\sqrt{3} + 6\sqrt{3} - 4\sqrt{6} = 10\sqrt{6} - 4\sqrt{6} - 5\sqrt{3} + 6\sqrt{3}$$
$$= (10 - 4)\sqrt{6} + (-5 + 6)\sqrt{3}$$
$$= 6\sqrt{6} + \sqrt{3}$$

Example 2: Simplify $3\sqrt{12} + 5\sqrt{75}$.

$$3\sqrt{12} + 5\sqrt{75} = 3\sqrt{2^2 \cdot 3} + 5\sqrt{5^2 \cdot 3}$$
$$= 3 \cdot 2\sqrt{3} + 5 \cdot 5\sqrt{3}$$
$$= 6\sqrt{3} + 25\sqrt{3}$$
$$= (6 + 25)\sqrt{3}$$
$$= 31\sqrt{3}$$

Simplify. Then use a calculator to verify your answer.

1. $8 + 3\sqrt{2}$
$8 + 3\sqrt{2}$;
$8 + 4.24 = 12.24$

2. $\sqrt{12} - \sqrt{27}$
$-\sqrt{3}$; 3.46 −
5.20 ≈ −1.73

3. $\sqrt{27} - 2\sqrt{3}$
$\sqrt{3}$; 5.20 −
3.46 ≈ 1.73

4. $\sqrt{20} + 2\sqrt{5} - 3\sqrt{5}$
$\sqrt{5}$; 4.47 + 4.47 −
6.71 ≈ 2.24

5. $-5\sqrt{6} + 8\sqrt{6}$
$3\sqrt{6}$; −12.25 +
19.60 = 7.35

6. $\sqrt{200} - 3\sqrt{2}$
$7\sqrt{2}$; 14.14 −
4.24 = 9.90

7. $\sqrt{54} + \sqrt{24}$
$5\sqrt{6}$; 7.35 + 4.90 =
12.25

8. $\sqrt{18} - 3\sqrt{8} + \sqrt{50}$
$2\sqrt{2}$; 4.24 − 8.49 +
7.07 ≈ 2.83

9. $\sqrt{80} - \sqrt{20} + \sqrt{180}$
$8\sqrt{5}$; 8.94 − 4.47 +
13.42 = 17.89

10. $2\sqrt{28} + 3\sqrt{63} - \sqrt{\dfrac{54}{3}}$
$13\sqrt{7} - 3\sqrt{2}$;
10.58 + 23.81 −
4.24 = 30.15 =
34.39 − 4.24

11. $\sqrt{12} + \sqrt{\dfrac{1}{3}}$
$\dfrac{7\sqrt{3}}{3}$; 3.46 +
0.58 = 4.04

12. $\sqrt{54} - \sqrt{\dfrac{1}{6}} + \sqrt{24}$
$\dfrac{29}{6}\sqrt{6}$; 7.35 −
0.41 + 4.90 = 11.84

Study Guide

Radical Equations

Solve radical equations (equations containing radicals with variables in the radicand) as follows.

a. Isolate the radical on one side of the equation.

b. Then square each side of the equation to eliminate the radical.

Example: Solve $\sqrt{4x - 7} - 5 = 0$.

$$\sqrt{4x - 7} - 5 = 0$$
$$\sqrt{4x - 7} = 5$$
$$4x - 7 = 25$$
$$4x = 32$$
$$x = 8$$

Check the solution by substituting 8 into the original equation.

Solve each equation. Check your solution.

1. $\sqrt{2y} = 4$

2. $2\sqrt{x} = 8$

3. $7 = \sqrt{26 - n}$

4. $\sqrt{3r^2} = -3$

5. $\sqrt{6x^2 + 5x} = 2$

6. $\sqrt{4n^2} = \frac{1}{3}$

7. $\sqrt{10 - 6k} + 3 = k$

8. $r - 2\sqrt{5 - 2r} = 4$

9. $\sqrt{5m - 2} = \sqrt{3}$

10. $\sqrt{\frac{x}{2}} = \frac{1}{2}$

11. $-2\sqrt{\frac{z}{8}} = 15$

12. $\sqrt{\frac{x}{3}} = 2$

Study Guide

Radical Equations

Solve radical equations (equations containing radicals with variables in the radicand) as follows.

a. Isolate the radical on one side of the equation.
b. Then square each side of the equation to eliminate the radical.

Example: Solve $\sqrt{4x-7} - 5 = 0$.

$$\sqrt{4x-7} - 5 = 0$$
$$\sqrt{4x-7} = 5$$
$$4x - 7 = 25$$
$$4x = 32$$
$$x = 8$$

Check the solution by substituting 8 into the original equation.

Solve each equation. Check your solution.

1. $\sqrt{2y} = 4$
8

2. $2\sqrt{x} = 8$
16

3. $7 = \sqrt{26 - n}$
−23

4. $\sqrt{3r^2} = -3$
∅

5. $\sqrt{6x^2 + 5x} = 2$
$\frac{1}{2}, -\frac{4}{3}$

6. $\sqrt{4n^2} = \frac{1}{3}$
$-\frac{1}{6}, \frac{1}{6}$

7. $\sqrt{10 - 6k} + 3 = k$
∅

8. $r - 2\sqrt{5 - 2r} = 4$
∅

9. $\sqrt{5m - 2} = \sqrt{3}$
1

10. $\sqrt{\frac{x}{2}} = \frac{1}{2}$
$\frac{1}{2}$

11. $-2\sqrt{\frac{z}{8}} = 15$
∅

12. $\sqrt{\frac{x}{3}} = 2$
12

Study Guide

Integration: Geometry
The Distance Formula

The Pythagorean theorem can be used to derive the distance formula shown at the right. The distance formula can then be used to find the distance between any two points in the coordinate plane.

The Distance Formula
The distance between any two points with coordinates (x_1, y_1) and (x_2, y_2) is given by the following formula. $$d = \sqrt{(x_2 - x_1)^2 + (y_2 - y_1)^2}$$

Example: Find the distance between $(-5, 2)$ and $(4, 5)$.

In the diagram at the right below, the distance to be found is d. Use the distance formula.

$$d = \sqrt{(x_2 - x_1)^2 + (y_2 - y_1)^2}$$
$$= \sqrt{[4 - (-5)]^2 + (5 - 2)^2}$$
$$= \sqrt{9^2 + 3^2}$$
$$= \sqrt{81 + 9}$$
$$= \sqrt{90} = 3\sqrt{10}$$

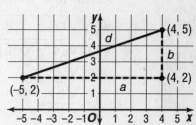

The distance is $3\sqrt{10}$ units.

Find the distance between each pair of points whose coordinates are given. Express answers in simplest radical form and as decimal approximations rounded to the nearest hundredth.

1. $(1, 5), (3, 1)$

2. $(0, 0), (6, 8)$

3. $(-2, -8), (7, -3)$

4. $(6, -7), (-2, 8)$

5. $(1, 5), (-8, 4)$

6. $(3, -4), (-4, -4)$

Find the value of a if the points with the given coordinates are the indicated distance apart.

7. $(-3, -2), (a, -5); d = 5$

8. $(2, -1), (a, 3); d = 5$

9. $(a, 3), (2, -4); d = \sqrt{74}$

Study Guide

Integration: Geometry
The Distance Formula

The Pythagorean theorem can be used to derive the distance formula shown at the right. The distance formula can then be used to find the distance between any two points in the coordinate plane.

The Distance Formula
The distance between any two points with coordinates (x_1, y_1) and (x_2, y_2) is given by the following formula. $$d = \sqrt{(x_2 - x_1)^2 + (y_2 - y_1)^2}$$

Example: Find the distance between $(-5, 2)$ and $(4, 5)$.

In the diagram at the right below, the distance to be found is d. Use the distance formula.

$$d = \sqrt{(x_2 - x_1)^2 + (y_2 - y_1)^2}$$
$$= \sqrt{[4 - (-5)]^2 + (5 - 2)^2}$$
$$= \sqrt{9^2 + 3^2}$$
$$= \sqrt{81 + 9}$$
$$= \sqrt{90} = 3\sqrt{10}$$

The distance is $3\sqrt{10}$ units.

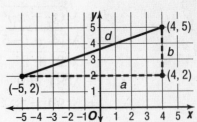

Find the distance between each pair of points whose coordinates are given. Express answers in simplest radical form and as decimal approximations rounded to the nearest hundredth.

1. $(1, 5), (3, 1)$
   $2\sqrt{5}$; **4.47**

2. $(0, 0), (6, 8)$
   10

3. $(-2, -8), (7, -3)$
   $\sqrt{106}$; **10.30**

4. $(6, -7), (-2, 8)$
   17

5. $(1, 5), (-8, 4)$
   $\sqrt{82}$; **9.06**

6. $(3, -4), (-4, -4)$
   7

Find the value of a if the points with the given coordinates are the indicated distance apart.

7. $(-3, -2), (a, -5); d = 5$
   −7 or 1

8. $(2, -1), (a, 3); d = 5$
   −1 or 5

9. $(a, 3), (2, -4); d = \sqrt{74}$
   −3 or 7

Solving Quadratic Equations by Completing the Square

Equations containing quadratic expressions that are not perfect squares can be solved by a method called *completing the square*. To complete the square for an expression of the form $x^2 + bx$, follow the steps listed below.

Completing the Square for an Expression of the Form $x^2 + bx$
Step 1 Find one-half of b, the coefficient of x.
Step 2 Square the result of **Step 1**.
Step 3 Add the result of **Step 2** to $x^2 + bx$.

Example: Solve $x^2 + 2x - 15 = 0$ by completing the square.

$$x^2 + 2x - 15 = 0 \qquad \text{$x^2 + 2x - 15$ is not a perfect square.}$$
$$x^2 + 2x = 15 \qquad \text{Add 15 to each side.}$$
$$x^2 + 2x + 1 = 15 + 1 \qquad \text{Complete the square for $x^2 + 2x$.}$$
$$(x + 1)^2 = 16 \qquad \text{Factor $x^2 + 2x + 1$.}$$
$$x + 1 = \pm 4 \qquad \text{Find the square root of each side.}$$
$$x = \pm 4 - 1 \qquad \text{Subtract 1 from each side.}$$
$$x = -4 - 1 \quad \text{or} \quad x = 4 - 1$$
$$x = -5 \qquad\qquad x = 3$$

The solution set is $\{-5, 3\}$.

Solve each equation by completing the square. Leave irrational roots in simplest radical form.

1. $y^2 + 6y + 5 = 0$ **2.** $r^2 + 4r - 21 = 0$ **3.** $y^2 + 8y + 15 = 0$

4. $x^2 - 12x + 35 = 0$ **5.** $3y^2 - 2y - 1 = 0$ **6.** $d^2 + 3d - 18 = 0$

7. $n^2 + 16n + 14 = 0$ **8.** $t^2 - 2t = 15$ **9.** $-2x^2 + 10x + 22 = 0$

Study Guide

Student Edition
Pages 743–747

Solving Quadratic Equations by Completing the Square

Equations containing quadratic expressions that are not perfect squares can be solved by a method called *completing the square*. To complete the square for an expression of the form $x^2 + bx$, follow the steps listed below.

Completing the Square for an Expression of the Form $x^2 + bx$
Step 1 Find one-half of b, the coefficient of x.
Step 2 Square the result of **Step 1**.
Step 3 Add the result of **Step 2** to $x^2 + bx$.

Example: Solve $x^2 + 2x - 15 = 0$ by completing the square.

$$x^2 + 2x - 15 = 0 \qquad \text{$x^2 + 2x - 15$ is not a perfect square.}$$
$$x^2 + 2x = 15 \qquad \text{Add 15 to each side.}$$
$$x^2 + 2x + 1 = 15 + 1 \qquad \text{Complete the square for $x^2 + 2x$.}$$
$$(x + 1)^2 = 16 \qquad \text{Factor $x^2 + 2x + 1$.}$$
$$x + 1 = \pm 4 \qquad \text{Find the square root of each side.}$$
$$x = \pm 4 - 1 \qquad \text{Subtract 1 from each side.}$$
$$x = -4 - 1 \quad \text{or} \quad x = 4 - 1$$
$$x = -5 \qquad\qquad x = 3$$

The solution set is $\{-5, 3\}$.

Solve each equation by completing the square. Leave irrational roots in simplest radical form.

1. $y^2 + 6y + 5 = 0$
   $-1, -5$

2. $r^2 + 4r - 21 = 0$
   $-7, 3$

3. $y^2 + 8y + 15 = 0$
   $-5, -3$

4. $x^2 - 12x + 35 = 0$
   $5, 7$

5. $3y^2 - 2y - 1 = 0$
   $-\dfrac{1}{3}, 1$

6. $d^2 + 3d - 18 = 0$
   $-6, 3$

7. $n^2 + 16n + 14 = 0$
   $-8 \pm 5\sqrt{2}$

8. $t^2 - 2t = 15$
   $-3, 5$

9. $-2x^2 + 10x + 22 = 0$
   $\dfrac{5 \pm \sqrt{69}}{2}$